Get Fit for
Orienteering

Get Fit for
Orienteering

by Steve Bird

**Principal Lecturer in Sport Science
Canterbury Christ Church College,
Kent, England**

Nonington Press

First published in 1996 by
Nonington Press
Canterbury, Kent, UK

British Library Cataloguing in Publication Data

A catalogue record for this book is available from the British Library

ISBN 0-95273-510-5

Steve Bird is an accredited exercise physiologist lecturing at Canterbury Christ Church College, in Kent, England.

He is also the director of a British Association of Sport and Exercise Sciences accredited laboratory and Sport Science Support Programme, which conducts physiological assessments on performers from various sports and provides advice on fitness training methods.

His work includes published research in sport science and support work with athletes of various sports.

Edited, designed and typeset by CompassSport Publications,
37 Sandycoombe Road, Twickenham, TW1 2LR Tel: 0181-892 9429

Printed in Great Britain by the Bath Press

Contents

Foreword

by Mike Murray

British Open Champion 1972, British Age Group Champion 1985, 1990, 1992.
JK Age Group Winner 1981, 1986, 1991, 1994, 1995.
World Championship competitor 1966, 1972, 1974.

In our intriguing and constantly challenging sport, finding the control sites is a relatively easy task. Getting through the following week and preparing for the next event is far more difficult. If you want to maximise on your potential you will have to get and then stay fit. After all the only time success comes before work is in the dictionary.

This means training on a regular basis and probably in the fag end time of the day. No matter which session you choose, the hardest bit is always at the beginning – getting out of the front door.

Don't let me put you off – the benefits of training are life enhancing and Steve Bird is uniquely qualified to explain how to go about it. After a well spent youth in athletics, cross country and road running - he represented the AAA in steeplechase – Steve and his wife Jackie took to orienteering and both have improved to represent England. His sports science background ensures that all the training hints and programmes have a sound physiological basis. And lastly he has a great enthusiasm for his subject and his sport. He has always shared his knowledge with others and this book fills a large gap on the orienteering bookshelf.

PART ONE

Fitness Basics

Chapter 1.1
Fitness Facts

Fit for orienteering - the fitness requirements of orienteering - the components of an orienteer's fitness - aerobic fitness and muscular endurance - muscular strength and anaerobic power - flexibility and suppleness - the importance of warming up - summary

Fit for orienteering

To be a good orienteer you must be fit enough to cope with the physical demands of the sport. The fitter you are, the faster you can cover the distance and the less likely you are to make mistakes due to excessive fatigue.

Getting fit for orienteering is not just a matter of competing on a Sunday and going out for a few runs or gym sessions during the week. Orienteering is unique, and whilst the fitness requirements are similar to that of cross country and fell running they are not quite the same. To get fit for orienteering you have to train like an orienteer. That is not to say that other activities cannot help with your fitness, but they need to be incorporated into a balanced programme geared up to getting you fit for orienteering; not competitive swimming, cycling or weight lifting.

What is it then that makes the fitness requirements of orienteering different from those of other sports? To understand this we have to look at the physical demands of orienteering, what makes up our fitness and how by improving these fitness components we become more able to cope.

The fitness requirements of orienteering

Orienteering is primarily an endurance running activity. However, unlike other running events the terrain tends to be rougher and far more varied. Within a single event an orienteer may have to cope with undergrowth, brashings, rutted ground, dodge through dense trees and cross marshes, as well as run along paths. All of which make special demands of the orienteer and require a specific type of fitness.

This means that if you spend all your training time running along a road it will not prepare you completely for orienteering; a fact which many good road and cross country runners have experienced when trying the sport. For example, it is very often the case that a good road runner will be faster than an orienteer when on the paths but on entering the forest they struggle to keep up.

Another difference is that unlike most other running events, the speed at which an orienteer runs during an event varies very considerably. Orienteers may slow down when moving into a technically difficult area or approaching a control and then speed up again in a fast open area. These changes in pace need to be trained for.

Then of course there are the hills; minutes can be gained if you are fit enough to run up the hills and just as important is the time you save by not making silly errors through fatigue when you reach the top.

To perform well orienteers need a good aerobic capacity and good muscular endurance to keep going throughout what would generally be considered a long distance race. They also need good muscular strength for running up hills, over soft ground and through thick undergrowth. Finally, they need a certain amount of flexibility to move fluently over rough terrain. To be fit for orienteering an orienteer must train each of these fitness components in a way that is specific to the sport.

This does not mean that everyone has to train in the same way. Fitness is relative to the individual and the level at which he or she wishes to participate. In orienteering an elite woman runner taking part in W21E at a national event has to deal with greater physical demands than a woman on the shorter W21S. Both must train in a way which prepares them for their event, so that if she is fit the W21E competitor will cope as easily with the demands imposed by her course as will the W21S who may find the shorter course just as demanding for her own more modest level of fitness.

So when planning to get fit you need to decide the level at which you

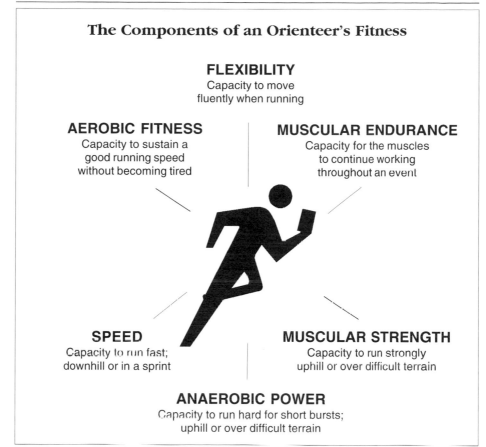

The Components of an Orienteer's Fitness

FLEXIBILITY
Capacity to move
fluently when running

AEROBIC FITNESS
Capacity to sustain a
good running speed
without becoming tired

MUSCULAR ENDURANCE
Capacity for the muscles
to continue working
throughout an event

SPEED
Capacity to run fast;
downhill or in a sprint

MUSCULAR STRENGTH
Capacity to run strongly
uphill or over difficult terrain

ANAEROBIC POWER
Capacity to run hard for short bursts;
uphill or over difficult terrain

intend to compete and train for it accordingly. Remember that the fitter you are, the more likely you are to produce your best possible performance.

Most people will possess the physical fitness needed to cope with the demands of orienteering at a basic level. To progress in the sport this basic fitness must be enhanced and developed by training. The higher you wish to go in the sport, the more important this training becomes.

The components of an orienteer's fitness

Before considering the type of training an orienteer should do we must identify the special fitness qualities needed. An orienteer's fitness is made up of many different components including:

- Aerobic fitness and muscular endurance
- Muscular strength and anaerobic power
- Flexibility and suppleness

and of course speed over the terrain.

In orienteering it is an individual's aerobic fitness and muscular endurance which are of key importance as these

11

have the greatest influence in determining the maximum running speed that an orienteer can sustain throughout the event.

In addition to this an appropriate level of muscular strength and anaerobic power are an advantage as these will provide the capacity to run strongly uphill, through rough undergrowth and over boggy ground.

Similarly an ability to move relatively quickly through the forest requires a combination of speed and agility which is more important than flat out sprinting speed (although this could have its advantages in the finishing lane!).

Finally a certain amount of flexibility and suppleness is needed in orienteering. It is not as extreme as that needed in sports such as gymnastics, but it should be sufficient to permit a fluent running action. A func-

tional level of flexibility will also reduce the risk of injury, which is more likely to occur if your muscles are tight and unsupple.

Aerobic fitness and muscular endurance

Orienteering is primarily an endurance sport which involves running relatively long distances as quickly as possible. It therefore requires a high level of endurance fitness, also referred to as stamina.

The running speed which can be sustained by an orienteer is largely determined by how much oxygen the muscles can use, a factor known as 'aerobic capacity'. When running comfortably within our aerobic capacity we can keep going for a long time. However, the faster we run the more oxygen we need, and if we try to run above our aerobic capacity then our muscles produce large amounts of lactic acid. This is what causes that fatigued burning sensation in our legs and forces us to slow down. The details of this are described more fully in chapter 1.2.

So what the orienteer needs is a large capacity to use oxygen, to be able to run quickly without producing lactic acid. This is best developed by the different types of running training described in Part 3.

Muscular strength and anaerobic power

An appropriate level of functional strength and anaerobic power helps when running uphill or over rough ground. To be able to run 'strongly' in this type of terrain all the muscles need to be in a good condition, not just those of the legs. General conditioning exercises and circuit training can be used to develop the general condition of the abdominal and upper body musculature as well as strengthening the leg muscles.

As indicated previously, flat out sprinting speed is not essential for orienteering, but a certain amount of speed and power are required to move rapidly and agilely through the forest. Anaerobic power is needed to give you this speed as well as providing some of the energy to run uphill. Training for these more intensive bursts of activity is probably best achieved by performing hill repetitions and interval training, both of which will make demands upon your body's anaerobic metabolism and thus induce a training effect upon it.

So while aerobic fitness and muscular endurance may be the key fitness components, the orienteer's need to run powerfully uphill or over rough terrain makes a good level of strength and anaerobic power important.

Flexibility and suppleness

Most orienteers could be more flexible and therefore some flexibility work should be included as part of your warm up before each training session or race. However, if substantial improvements are desired some specific flexibility sessions should be included in your training programme.

The importance of warming up

A bout of exercise should start gradually with the change from rest to walking to jogging, to steady running to running hard being spread over several minutes. This allows the required cardiovascular responses to occur gradually, for example, the essential delivery of additional oxygen to the muscles.

To attempt to run quickly without warming up can cause problems. An increase in oxygen consumption cannot go from its resting level to maximum instantaneously. It needs a number of minutes in order to give the cardiovascular system time to adjust to the demands being placed upon it.

This is the major reason for warming up prior to any competition or hard training session. If these responses are gradually invoked during a warm up, the body will be ready for the start of the strenuous exercise and more able to cope with the rapid rise in

heart rate and ventilation demanded by the exercise.

Remember a warm up is not just about feeling warm. Many internal adjustments need to take place to prepare you for the exercise. A warm up reduces the risk of injury, since cold and unsupple muscles and tendons are more vulnerable to injury than those which are warm and flexible. Additionally a proper warm up can also help to prepare you mentally for the event.

Summary

● A large capacity to utilise oxygen (VO$_2$ max) is the general basis of an orienteer's fitness. Not only is it important during an event but it will also help during other forms of training and enable you to recover during activities such as circuit training.

● You must also be able to work anaerobically for short periods, as when running uphill. To do this you need to keep all your muscles in a good condition.

● Regular training such as steady continuous running, or the more strenuous forms of training such as interval work, is required to promote improvements in fitness. In the case of the already very fit, such regular training is necessary to maintain their high level of fitness.

● Don't forget to include a warm up phase in all training sessions or you may find the early stages unnecessarily tiring and unproductive.

● Think about what you are asking your body to do and give it a chance to adjust to the demands being asked of it.

● Most of all plan your training so that you can achieve your fitness goals.

Chapter 1.2

The Physiology of Orienteering Fitness

Oxygen requirements for orienteers - lactic acid - VO_2 max - the physiological basis of aerobic fitness - summary

Oxygen requirements for orienteers

At rest our bodies need a relatively small amount of oxygen. This is supplied to the muscles and other organs of the body by breathing gently and maintaining a steady heart rate. Typical values may be in the region of 12 breaths per minute, each of about 0.5 litres of air, giving a ventilation of about 6 litres per minute. Note that this is air going in and out of the lungs, not the actual amount of oxygen getting into the body and being used by the body. This will be far less: perhaps in the region of 0.4litres or if we represent this in terms of body weight, about 5 millilitres of oxygen per kilogram of body weight per minute.

At rest the heart will deliver this oxygen with a heart rate of around 72 beats per minute, with each beat ejecting about 70ml of blood (a factor known as the *stroke volume*). This means that, at rest, the heart will eject 72 x 70ml of blood a minute, approximately 5 litres. The amount of blood ejected each minute is known as the *cardiac output*. Of this cardiac output, only about 20% is directed towards the muscles, since they are at rest and do not require much oxygen. The remainder is sent to other organs of the body such as the brain and gut.

When we start to exercise our muscles need more oxygen. If we walk

Fig 1. 2 (i)

Physiological responses to running at different speeds

The values given are typical of a fit orienteer (aged 19-40). The actual values will differ for anyone of a lower level of fitness but the trends shown in the responses will be similar. However, since capacity to use oxygen will be lower, the less fit orienteer will produce more lactic acid at the slower speeds and will not be able to sustain the faster speeds of the fit orienteer.

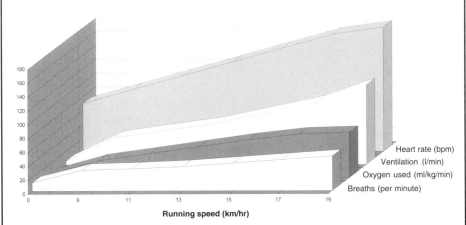

Running Speed	Oxygen Used (ml/kg/min.)	Breaths per min.	Ventilation (litres/min.)	Heart Rate (bpm)
Rest (0km/h)	5	12	6	70
Jog (9km/h)	25	30	40	90
Run Gently (11km/h)	35	32	50	110
Run Steadily (13km/h)	45	35	60	130
Run Moderately Hard (15km/h)	55	40	75	150
Run Hard (17km/h)	63*	45	90	170
Run Very Hard (19km/h)	65†	50	115	180

* At this speed, the individual is unable to provide their muscles with all of the energy they need via the use of oxygen (aerobically). Some of the energy must therefore be provided by other reactions (anaerobically), causing lactic acid to be produced. As this accumulates the runner experiences a significant level of fatigue.

† At this speed, the amount of energy derived from the runner's anaerobic systems is considerable. This results in the rapid production of large amounts of lactic acid, causing the runner to fatigue very quickly. The pace cannot be sustained for very long.

the increased demand for oxygen is slight and can be met by small increases in the rate and depth of breathing, accompanied by a slight increase in heart rate, perhaps up to 90bpm. If we jog there is a greater demand for oxygen and hence breathing will increase more dramatically and the heart rate may rise to 120 bpm. In addition to this the stroke volume of the heart will increase, causing more blood to be ejected with each beat, and furthermore a greater percentage of the cardiac output will be sent to the exercising muscles. This is achieved by the selective dilation of the blood vessels supplying the exercising muscles and a constriction of those supplying other organs such as the gut.

These changes are in proportion to the strenuousness of the exercise. For example, running at a steady pace requires a greater oxygen uptake and hence greater response by the cardiorespiratory system than gentle jogging. Indeed, when working close to a maximum sustainable running speed, the sort of speed that can be maintained for 1 or 2 minutes, very large responses are observed. Typical figures for a fit orienteer may be a heart rate of 180 - 190 bpm, a stroke volume of 120 - 140ml per beat, a cardiac output of 21.6 - 26.6 litres per minute, 75-80% of the cardiac output being directed to the exercising muscles and a ventilation of 140 - 160 litres of air per minute, with a resultant oxygen utilisation of 60 - 70ml/kg/min.

So to sustain a good running speed during an orienteering event we must be able to provide our muscles with large amounts of oxygen. This is achieved by getting the heart lungs and blood system to work harder. If we cannot deliver the required oxygen our muscles will soon tire and we have to slow down.

(Note: the figures given here are for a young, fit, male. The exact values will depend upon the size, age and gender of the individual, as well as their level of fitness.)

Lactic acid

As indicated in the previous section, when we run our muscles' need for oxygen is met by a faster heart rate, a more powerful pumping action of the heart and an increased ventilation of the lungs.

If we continue to increase our running speed, there is a point at which the muscles' demand for oxygen cannot be met. This is because everyone has a maximum possible heart rate: the heart and lungs are of finite capacity and there is a finite amount of oxygen that can be transported in the blood. The amount of oxygen that can be delivered to and utilised by the muscles is also finite.

If you attempt to run at speeds which require more oxygen than your body can deliver to the muscles, then you will need to use supplementary sources of energy. Your body achieves this by *anaerobic metabolism*. The problem with this is that it results in the formation of lactic acid. If this accumulates, it causes fatigue and forces you to slow down or stop.

An aerobically fit orienteer, with a greater capacity to use oxygen, can run at faster speeds without needing to resort to anaerobic metabolism. Where two individuals are running at the same speed, the fitter may be well within his or her aerobic capacity and therefore find the pace comfortable. At the same pace, the unfit individual may exceed aerobic capacity, start to accumulate lactic acid, feel fatigued and have to stop.

VO$_2$ max

The maximum running speed which an orienteer can sustain before this build up of lactic acid occurs is largely determined by the amount of oxygen able to be utilised; a factor referred to by physiologists as an individual's VO$_2$ max. This factor is commonly expressed in terms of the maximum amount of oxygen that a person can utilise per kilogram of body weight per minute and is therefore given in units of millilitres of oxygen per kilogram of body weight per minute (ml/kg/min). It can be measured in the laboratory.

Top orienteers, like other endurance runners or cyclists, have high VO$_2$ max values. Male international orienteers usually record values in excess of 70ml/kg/min, while female orienteers of a comparable level tend to have slightly lower values in the region of 60 - 70 ml/kg/min. Average VO$_2$ max values for the general population tend to be much lower, approximately 47ml/kg/min for males and 40ml/kg/min for females in the 21 - 34 age group. There is a slight decline in VO$_2$ max with age, due to a loss of cardiovascular function as part of the ageing process.

This goes some way towards explaining why the fastest and fittest orienteers tend to be in the 21 - 34 age group. However, there is also some evidence to suggest that by remaining active in sports such as orienteering, this age-related loss in physical capacity can be minimised.

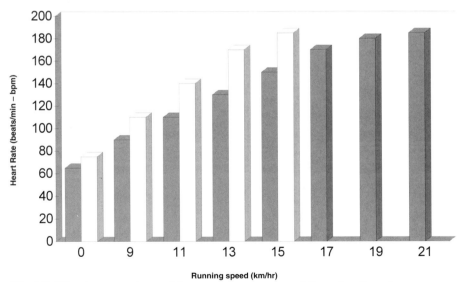

Running speed (km/hr)

Fig 1.2 (ii)   A comparison of heart rate responses of fit and unfit orienteers. The unfit orienteer, shown in the lighter colour, reaches maximum heart rate at a slower running speed. At the same heart rate the fit orienteer can maintain a faster speed.

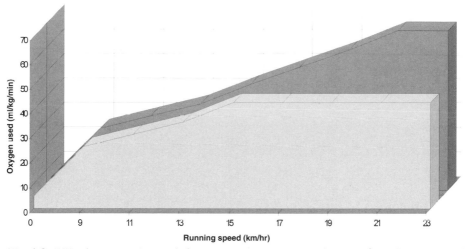

Fig 1.2 (iii) A comparison of the oxygen provision to the muscles of fit and unfit orienteers.

A fit orienteer can deliver and utilise more oxygen meaning a faster running speed can be maintained. If the unfit orienteer tries to run at the faster running speeds, the undersupply of oxygen causes a build up of lactic acid and resultant fatigue.

Generally speaking the fitter you are the higher your VO_2 max will be and the faster you will be able to run throughout an orienteering event. Note that it is the sustained pace throughout the event which is being considered here and not a brief sprint at the end, when the fitness requirements are anaerobic rather than aerobic and therefore unrelated to a person's ability to utilise oxygen.

The Physiological Basis of Aerobic Fitness

The various stages by which oxygen is delivered to and used by the muscles are:

1. Breathing. This is the process by which air containing about 20.9% oxygen is sucked into the lungs. It is the first stage in determining an individual's capacity to use oxygen. A large lung volume, clear airways and effective respiratory muscles, such as the diaphragm and intercostals, which are situated between the ribs and are used in the process of breathing, will be an advantage.

However, unless an individual suffers from a respiratory disorder such as asthma, the capacity to get air in and out of the lungs is not likely to be the limiting factor in determining VO_2 max and hence aerobic fitness.

2. Carriage of Oxygen by the Blood. When in the lungs the air travels down the airways which divide into smaller and smaller branches until they terminate in tiny airsacs called alveoli.

It is estimated that these millions of alveoli give the lungs a surface area

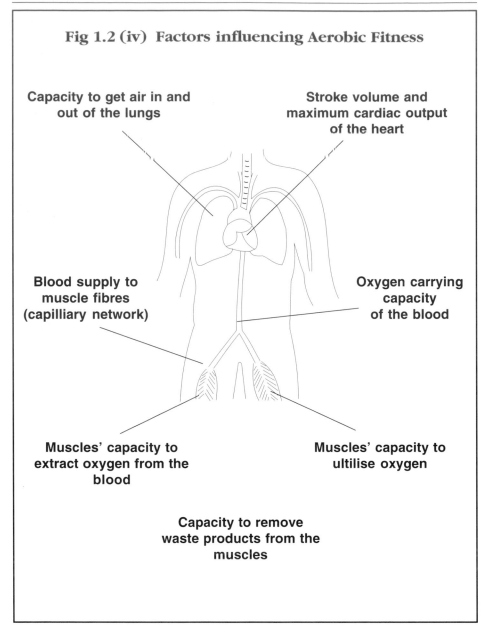

Fig 1.2 (iv) Factors influencing Aerobic Fitness

Capacity to get air in and out of the lungs

Stroke volume and maximum cardiac output of the heart

Blood supply to muscle fibres (capilliary network)

Oxygen carrying capacity of the blood

Muscles' capacity to extract oxygen from the blood

Muscles' capacity to ultilise oxygen

Capacity to remove waste products from the muscles

similar to that of a tennis court. Each of the alveoli are surrounded by tiny blood vessels called capillaries. The oxygen arriving in the alveoli diffuses across the walls of the alveoli into the blood where it is picked up by the red blood cells. In the red blood cells the oxygen combines with molecules of haemoglobin.

At the same time the carbon dioxide which has been produced by the body diffuses out of the blood into the alveoli to be removed from the body when we breath out.

The amount of oxygen which can be carried by the blood depends upon an individual's blood volume, the number of red blood cells they have and the amount of haemoglobin they contain. A high value for each of these factors will enable the individual to transport large amounts of oxygen around their body. Fortunately, one of the effects of training is an increase in these factors, thereby improving an individual's capacity to deliver oxygen to their exercising muscles.

Normally this increase is stimulated by the hormone erythropoetin which naturally promotes the production of more red blood cells when required. You may have read, however, of this process being abused and enhanced by the use of drugs such as EPO, which artificially stimulates the body to produce more red blood cells, thereby supplementing the natural effects of training and the naturally occurring increases in red blood cells.

Blood doping has a similar effect and involves artificially increasing a person's blood volume by infusing extra blood before a competition. The source of this additional blood may be the individual concerned, in which case it will have been removed some months earlier and then stored, or in some reported cases taken from a relative with the same blood type.

When discussing the oxygen carrying capacity of the blood it should be mentioned that smokers significantly disadvantage themselves by reducing this factor. This is because the smoke they inhale contains carbon monoxide which binds to the haemo-

globin preventing the oxygen from attaching to it and hence greatly reducing the blood's oxygen carrying capacity. The nearer to an event a person smokes the greater the detriment will be to performance.

3. Pumping of the Heart. The blood is pumped through the blood vessels and around the body by the action of the heart. Training can make the heart stronger and more efficient, enabling it to eject more blood with each beat. This means that, if required to, the heart can deliver a far greater amount of blood and hence oxygen to the muscles. Thus an individual with a large strong heart will be able to deliver more oxygen and should be able to sustain a faster running pace during an event.

At any given submaximal running speed, the fitter, more powerful heart has to beat less often in order to deliver the necessary blood and oxygen to the muscles.

4. Blood supply to the muscle. The blood and oxygen is delivered to the muscles via the blood vessels. If these are in good condition then the passage of blood through them should be relatively easy. If they are constricted by factors such as fatty deposits (artheroma) then the delivery of the blood will be impeded. This has implications for advocating an all-round healthy lifestyle which includes plenty of exercise, not smoking and eating a diet which is relatively low in fat. Fortunately, activities such as ori-

enteering fulfil the criteria of being a healthy form of exercise and can therefore help to prevent the build up of fatty deposits on the walls of the blood vessels.

As the main blood vessels (arteries) reach the muscles they divide into smaller and smaller vessels until they eventually form capillaries. There are millions of these tiny vessels within each muscle. They provide it with an extensive network of blood vessels for the delivery of oxygen and nutrients as well as the removal of waste products.

As the blood passes through these capillaries it releases much of its oxygen and picks up certain metabolic waste products such as carbon dioxide and lactic acid. The carbon dioxide is delivered to the lungs from which it is exhaled, while the lactic acid is buffered and delivered to other tissues to be converted into other substances.

Aerobically fit or endurance trained muscles possess a more extensive capillary network than unfit muscles. This means that a greater amount of oxygen can be delivered more rapidly to the muscle fibres which need it. Again, training can promote the development of this capillary network and hence enhance the effective delivery of oxygen to the muscles.

5. Extraction of Oxygen from the Blood and its Utilisation by Muscle. The process of extracting oxygen from the blood and getting it into the muscle is aided by the presence of certain chemicals within the muscle, such as myoglobin. Aerobically fit muscle will have high levels of myoglobin thereby making the muscle more efficient at extracting the oxygen from the blood which passes through it.

Once in the muscle fibres, the oxygen is used to release the energy that is required for the muscles to contract. This energy is contained within the fats and sugars (carbohydrates) that have been delivered to the muscle for this purpose. When oxygen is used in the breakdown of carbohydrates a large amount of energy is released. Carbon dioxide is produced as a waste product, along with water.

The capacity of the muscle to utilise the oxygen in this manner is determined by the concentrations of various enzymes and organelles, such as mitochondria, within the muscle. Mitochondria are about the size of bac-

teria and are the site of oxygen utilisation. Endurance training will promote an increase in their size and number, thereby enhancing the muscle's capacity to utilise the oxygen. There is no point in the cardiovascular system delivering more oxygen to the muscles if they cannot make use of it.

6. Muscle Fibre types. Some muscle fibre types are highly suited to the process of breaking down fats and carbohydrates in the presence of oxygen (aerobically). They can be referred to as aerobic fibres (also known as red, or slow twitch, or type 1 fibres). Other muscle fibres are more suited to breaking down glucose without the use of oxygen (anaerobically). These are referred to as anaerobic fibres (also known as white, or fast twitch, or type

2 fibres). These latter fibres are more important when sprinting and play a less significant role during endurance activities, although they are likely to be recruited during intensive activities such as running uphill.

All our muscles are made up of a mixture of these different types of fibres. Some people have very high proportions of the aerobic fibres, making them ideally suited to endurance events. Others have very high proportions of anaerobic fibres which makes them well suited to activities which require more power such as sprinting rather than sustained endurance.

Whether we are born with these relative proportions and/or to what extent training can influence them is a matter of debate amongst physiologists.

7. Removal of Metabolic Waste Products. A fit aerobic muscle with a good blood supply will not only receive large amounts of oxygen but will also be able to rapidly remove the fatigue inducing waste products such as carbon dioxide and lactic acid.

Summary

● Aerobic fitness is a key determinant of orienteering performance. It is made up of a large number of physiological factors, many of which can be improved by appropriate training.

● For the orienteer an important issue is how to make training really effective in increasing aerobic capacity. To do this, training must be planned. How to go about it is covered in Part 2.

PART TWO

Planning Your Training

Chapter 2.1

The Principles of Training

Overload - specificity - intensity - duration - frequency - recovery - progression - reversibility - periodisation

The Principles of Training

To get the most benefit from your training, you need to apply the principles of training which are as follows:

1. Overload
2. Specificity
3. Intensity
4. Duration
5. Frequency
6. Recovery
7. Progression
8. Reversibility
9. Periodisation

Overload

The rationale for fitness training is to promote improvements in the physical condition of the body. Exercise is the stimulus which promotes these improvements. In order to stimulate the desired changes, your body has to experience a certain amount of physiological stress. That is to say, it has to work harder than it normally does in everyday life.

For example, to stimulate improvements in the condition of your cardiovascular system (heart and blood) you have to make your heart beat harder and faster. For the orienteer this is usually achieved by running.

Likewise to increase the strength of your muscles you have to make them work against harder resistances than they would normally encounter. Examples of strengthening regimens would be weight training or circuit training exercises. Here a certain amount of local muscular endurance work can also be built into the activity by doing a relatively high number of repetitions.

To improve your flexibility you have to stretch your muscles and move your joints through a greater range of movement than usual. This is achieved by performing specific loosening and stretching exercises.

Each of these activities provides the overload needed to produce improvements in the indicated aspects of your fitness. If applied correctly they will improve your performance.

Specificity

Specificity refers to the fact that any improvements in your fitness will be related to the type of training you do. For example, doing sit ups will enhance the condition of your abdominal muscles but not that of your arms. Similarly, stretching the hamstrings will improve the flexibility of that muscle group but not others.

Specificity of change in aerobic fitness is not quite that simple: the improvements may be classified as central (those occurring in the heart, blood and lungs) and peripheral (those occurring in the muscles). In general it is recognised that almost any form of aerobic exercise (jogging, cycling, swimming and aerobics) will promote central improvements to the condition of the cardiovascular system, but changes in the muscles (peripheral improvements) will only take place in those used in the activity and will be specific to that activity. This is why runners spend most of their time running, swimmers swimming and cyclists cycling.

This is not to preclude other activities from a fitness training programme and indeed, on occasions, they may be beneficial. For example runners can swim if they have an injury, as this will help to maintain a certain amount of cardiovascular fitness. Another reason for doing other forms of training is to try to prevent staleness and overuse injuries, which can occur if one activity is repeated too often. But in terms of fitness for orienteering, other activities will not be as effective as running, since the muscles are used in different movements and differ in their relative contribution to the activity.

In the case of orienteering, the concept of specificity extends beyond the need to run and includes a consideration of the terrain which is being run over. Many runners are fast along the paths, but it requires a special kind of fitness and technique to run fast over rough terrain and dodge trees at speed. This is only achieved by training over rough terrain and in forests, therefore all orienteers should spend at least some of their training time off the paths.

Intensity

The intensity of training refers to how hard you make it. This should reflect the intensity of the activity. In the case of orienteering it is a sustained prolonged effort and not a 100m sprint. On the other hand it is run at more than a gentle jog. Therefore much of your steady running should be at a pace which reflects your racing speed.

Those who are familiar with the idea may use their heart rate as a gauge of exercise intensity and, although it can be extremely variable between individuals, somewhere between 65 and 85% of your maximum heart rate is often used as a rough guide for your 'training zone'.

While some form of steady running will form the basis of orienteering training, orienteering courses require you to run at a variety of intensities. Phases of harder work, such as running uphill or over rough ground are mixed in with slightly easier spells, such as running downhill or running on a path as you recover from a period of high exertion. Again training should reflect this with the inclusion of hills and intervals.

Interval training may be organised in a number of ways: fartlek, paarlauf relays or set designated intervals. They all work on a similar principle of interspersing periods of high intensity running with phases of recovery, usually in the form of easy jogging. The basis behind this form of training is that it requires the cardio-vascular system to work harder than it would on a steady run, thereby providing extra overload.

For example, when doing an interval session of 12 two minute efforts with a one minute jog recovery between each one, or a hill session of 12 hills with a jog recovery between each one, your heart rate may well be in excess of 180bpm at the end of each of the 12 efforts. This is above the level which it is likely to reach during a steady run, so providing a greater stimulus for improvement.

Such training also requires the whole cardiovascular system to deliver oxygen as fast as it can to the muscles and makes them work beyond their maximum aerobic capacity, thereby providing an even greater training effect. You need to be reasonably fit before you even attempt this type of training, as it is very hard work and is certainly too tiring to do every day.

The concept of intensity applies equally to strengthening and stretching sessions. The intensity of strengthening exercises will be related to the number of repetitions being performed, but you should be working hard during the final few repetitions. If it is too easy then there will be little overload and you are unlikely to improve, although it may help to maintain strength. Conversely if the final few efforts are so hard that the muscles start to shake you must be careful not to overdo it and cause injury. Remember, you are trying to develop the level of muscular strength needed by a fit orienteer. You are not trying to become a competitive weightlifter.

The right intensity in stretching exercises may be described as a 'comfortable stretch'. Don't stretch to the point of pain (unless instructed otherwise by a suitably qualified medical practitioner) as this usually indicates too greater intensity and a risk of over-stretching, resulting in injury.

Duration

The duration of training should reflect the prolonged nature of orienteering.

To gain cardiovascular fitness a session should last for at least 20 minutes, although the actual duration will depend on your current level of fitness. If you are an unfit beginner, 20 minutes may be long enough, until you have become accustomed to the training. Conversely if you are a very fit orienteer then you are likely to be training for far longer, although it is not necessary to run for two hours every day, even if you are an elite orienteer, and especially not if you are including interval training in your running programme.

When referring to strengthening exercises, duration is often measured in repetitions, such as 20 sit ups or 30 press ups. With regard to flexibility training, the duration will refer to how long the stretched position is held for. This is usually a minimum of 10 seconds, but may be increased to over a minute.

Frequency

Doing one run, or one set of press ups, is unlikely to promote any improvements in your fitness. Improvements will only result if the exercise is of the correct type, intensity, duration and repeated often enough. Training once a week will be better than doing nothing, twice a week better still and three times a week even better.

However, there is a point of diminishing returns and, whilst additional sessions may continue to bring some benefit, the effects become less pronounced. The point this is reached depends on the individual and his or her level of fitness. Some orienteers appear to be able to train every day, whereas others function better on four runs a week. Just remember that even though three sessions a week may be good, 30 a week will not be ten times better. You have to find your own level.

Recovery

The point of training is to place certain physiological stresses on your body and then let it adapt. This is important – your body must be given the opportunity to adapt and recover.

This is because exercise can also cause a certain amount of unwanted physical stress, deplete energy reserves and cause damage to the muscles, tendons and joints, which if allowed to heal will go unnoticed. If it is not allowed to heal, then training with this unnoticed damage will cause further damage and the body tissues will start to break down. This is the typical scenario of an overuse injury.

Recovery must therefore be planned and incorporated into a training programme on a regular basis. Typically this will be a rest day during the week, or at least an easy day for those who insist on running everyday.

Overtraining can result in a decline in performance, injury, a loss of motivation, immune suppression and hormonal imbalances. It is a major problem with high level performers in many sports. Research has indicated a reduced incidence of injury in those who take regular rest days, and without a loss in fitness. Be wary of training hard on consecutive days and reduce your training prior to an important event; a procedure known as 'tapering' your training.

The term 'recovery' can also refer to that within a session as well as between sessions. In this context it may be used to describe the period of rest or easy jogging between intensive two minute efforts or hill repetition runs. Here the purpose of the recovery is to enable you to repeat the intensive burst of activity.

Progression

If your training is effective it will bring about improvements in your fitness. Your body will start to find the exercise easier and experience less overload. This is fine if you have achieved your desired level of fitness. If however you wish to continue to improve, you must once again place more overload on your body. This is referred to as 'progression' and should be applied carefully in a systematic manner.

Progression can be applied by increasing one or a combination of the following: (i) the intensity of the exercise (running faster), (ii) the duration of the exercise (running further) and (iii) the frequency of the exercise (running more often). Alternatively changing the type of terrain you run over can also increase the overload, by for example moving off the paths onto rough ground.

In the case of strengthening exercises, the resistance and repetitions may be increased or the exercise made more difficult such as by elevating the feet when doing press ups.

Progression must be applied gradually if the body is to be given time to adapt. Maximum increases of 10% a week or less are often advocated with regard to running mileage or repetitions.

Reversibility

This refers to the fact that if you stop training for a prolonged period of time your body starts to lose fitness and will revert to a more sedentary level.

But you don't need to worry about taking a few days off, as you will not lose much fitness in such a short time.

Indeed, a few days lay off whilst you are recovering from an illness or injury is essential and will do you more good than trying to continue training. When you do start training again don't try to go straight back to what you were doing before. Start at an easier level and build up gradually. This is even more significant if you've

31

had a long lay off, because your body will not be able to withstand the stresses you used to place upon it. Allow it time to regain its fitness and to adapt slowly over a period of weeks or even months.

Periodisation

Most training programmes will be divided up into phases such as:

   (i)   general conditioning

   (ii) event specific

   (iii) competition and

   (iv) recovery.

    General conditioning is the phase when you build up your fitness base by doing a relatively large volume of mileage and some strengthening work.

    This should get you fit for the intensive sport specific phase. The transition from the general conditioning phase should be gradual, with a steady increase in the intensity and frequency of the sessions. This is because of the greater demands that these sessions place upon your body and the necessity of letting it adapt gradually.

    In the competition phase the amount of training is reduced in both volume and intensity. In some cases training may be nearly halved. So your training should keep you just 'ticking over' providing a means of active recovery or fine tuning between events.

    The recovery phase occurs after the main competitions and enables both your mind and body to recover ready to start the cycle again. It may be in the form of a complete rest and holiday or a switch to a different activity for a few weeks.

    In the latter case be careful not to attempt new activities too vigorously. For example, playing basketball or tennis if you are not used to it places unfamiliar stresses on your body and you may get injured. Remember the principles of training even in the recovery phase.

    Throughout all the phases a certain amount of flexibility, strengthening and cardiovascular fitness work should be undertaken at all times to maintain these aspects of fitness. It is the relative intensity duration, frequency, volume, and emphasis of each which changes.

Chapter 2.2
Planning Your Training

Focusing your training - getting started - testing your fitness - designing a training programme - keeping a training diary - monitoring performance - summary

Focusing your training

Having outlined the principles of training, it is time to apply them to orienteering. This chapter looks at how you can work out your own training for the immediate months ahead, and beyond.

Getting fit for a particular sport is not just about "doing a bit of exercise". For training to be really effective it should be planned with definite aims and in accordance with the physical demands of that sport. If training isn't carefully thought out it is not likely to give you the best possible results. No exercise session should be undertaken as an isolated event, but should be part of a larger planned programme.

Training programmes are planned on a weekly, monthly, seasonal and in some cases, two to four year basis. They will usually involve a planned change of emphasis at different times of the year, a factor known as periodisation (discussed in chapters 2.1 and 3.2). This process is used by many top performers and coaches in all sports to try and 'peak' for the most important events.

Of course all training programmes must be flexible and modifications in-

corporated where necessary. For example, a slight illness may set you back a few weeks, in which case it is important to do a few easy sessions once you start training again and not try to catch up for lost time by attempting to do too much too soon. You may also find that you were over ambitious with your initial ideas and therefore need to modify the programme. Alternatively, if your training is going well, you may adjust your sights towards something more demanding.

Whatever training you are doing or planning for someone else, it must be considered alongside other commitments, such as work, family life, exams and so on. Think carefully about how you are going to fit it into your lifestyle and whether what you have set yourself is realistic.

Whenever you do a session remember to include a warm up and cool down, both of which are discussed at length in this book.

Getting Started

Having decided that you need to make your training specific to orienteering,

33

the most difficult step is often working out where to begin. To do this there are three things that you need to consider:

1. What are your goals?
2. How fit are you now?
3. What training are you doing now?

The answers to these three questions will be the starting point of your new training programme. One of the answers to question 1 will be "to get fitter" but this is rather imprecise and you may want to set a more specific goal. In order to do this you have to answer the second question by testing your fitness.

Testing Your Fitness

To get a direct measurement of your fitness a series of suggested tests are provided in Chapter 2.3. It is a good idea to do these straightaway rather than waiting until you have improved your fitness as this will give you a more realistic assessment of where you are now.

These fitness tests will give you a measurement of how long it takes you to run a certain distance over a particular type of terrain, providing an objective and quantifiable measurement of your current fitness. You can then set yourself a goal, such as to run the same course 30 seconds faster in 8 weeks time. Be realistic with your goals, make them challenging but do not expect huge improvements immediately.

Having measured your current level of fitness you will want to improve it. To do this you are going to have to make your training more effective. So the next thing to do is to write down the kind of training you are doing now and look to see how it can be improved.

For some orienteers this will simply mean doing more training than they are at present but this is not always the case. For example, if you are already running several times a week it could mean adjusting the type of training you do, so that it becomes more effective. A way of doing this could be to spend less time on the roads and more in the woods, or to include a few hard efforts and hill repetitions in a steady run.

So think about what training you are doing now and consider how it could be improved. To do this you have to have some appreciation of what the training is doing to your body and what benefits you are trying to get from it. So refer back to the principles of training. Relate these principles to your own training, and then make the adjustments which will make your own training more productive.

Designing a training programme

You may decide that the aim of your training programme is to get generally fitter for orienteering with no specific event in mind. In which case you can make your starting point tomorrow and gradually build up your training over a period of months.

Alternatively you may have a particular event or series of events in mind, for which you wish to 'peak'. If this is the case you will need to work backwards. Firstly, outline the kind of hard training programme you would hope to do when really fit. Then write down what you are doing now. Look at the difference and how much time you have got in which to build up to your peak of fitness. Finally fill in the details of what you are going to do each week as you gradually increase your training in your build up to this peak.

When doing this, remember to include an easy week immediately before the event. You cannot improve your fitness in the final week and may even ruin your chances if you train too hard and become too tired.

If you are planning 6-12 months in advance then you can apply the principle of periodisation - this is best illustrated with the aid of the diagram presented in chapter 3.3.

For every training session you should think about why you are doing the session and what your aims are. Then make sure that you have considered all the principles of training. This will help to ensure that you develop a systematic and effective training programme in a way that develops your fitness specifically for orienteering.

Keeping a training diary

When planning your training programme you should set out in detail what you intend to do over the next few months and outline your inten-

Fig 2.2 (i) Example of an orienteer's training diary

SUNDAY
Orienteering event 8.2k. Had a good run, able to push on and kept going up the hills. Still need to work on running over uneven ground. Quite warm and sunny for February but wind was cold.

MONDAY
Felt tired after yesterday's hard run.
a.m. Swam for 30 minutes (20 lengths)
p.m. Went to gym and did usual session for abdominals and upper body. gave legs a rest.

TUESDAY
Club training in park 12 x Monument Hill (total 8 miles) Getting better and kept up with the leaders for the first 6, started to fade towards the end.
(94, 95, 92, 96, 95, 94, 98, 101, 103, 104, 106, 99).
Cold wet night, be nice to do this session in daylight rather than under street lights.

WEDNESDAY
Steady run (6 miles). One lap of common and golf course. Ran steady and tried to do as much as possible off the paths in the rough (found 3 golf balls)

p.m. Circuit training session 3 x 12 stations; 30 seconds on, 30 recovery. Upper body is getting stronger, will move up to 40 on, 20 recovery for the 3rd circuit next week.

THURSDAY
Club night. Fuarlauf relay around perimeter road.
6 x 600m (approx) efforts
(115, 118, 116, 121, 123, 119).
Good group. ran hard (total 6 miles including warm up and warm down).

FRIDAY
Rest

SATURDAY
5k night event. Ran OK but difficult to see with the misty rain. Lunchtime meal of baked potato, beans and cheese seemed to be OK, didn't get a stitch - will have it again before next event.

Fig 2.2 (ii) Monitoring Performance

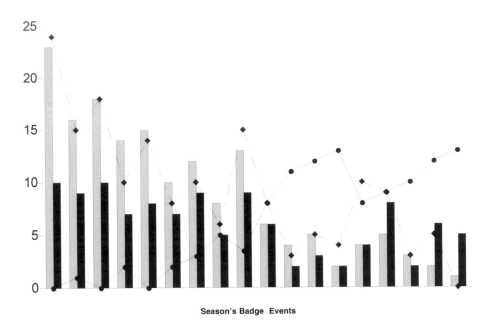

Season's Badge Events

In this diagram, an orienteer is shown monitoring performance using the following criteria: finishing position(light grey bar), time behind winner (dotted line), time inside gold standard (solid line) , and estimated time lost (dark bar). Note the improvement in this orienteer's performance during the season.

tions for perhaps up to a year in advance. In addition to this you should also keep a record of what you actually did in the form of a training diary.

One of the reasons for planning your training is to ensure that it contains a logical progression. However it is quite likely that you will need to modify your plans at various stages, due to the demands of your work or exams, family commitments and perhaps the occasional illness such as a cold or flu.

Your training diary should detail exactly what training you did rather than what you intended to do.

This information can help you to make sensible modifications to your programme, if for example you have to spend a few weeks doing some easy training before gradually building back up again. It is also a useful source of reference when looking back as it can tell you what worked last time. If you do not keep a detailed record you may have a tendency to only remember your best weeks or some exceptional sessions, rather than what you actually did most of the time.

When recording your running sessions try to note factors such as how far you ran, how long you took, the weather conditions and details of the interval efforts you ran. With other aspects of your training such as strengthening exercises you should include which exercises you did, how many repetitions, and if you used resistance machines, what resistance you used.

Use your diary to keep a daily record of all your training plus a summary at the end of each week or month. Within this you should also keep a record of your orienteering performances at badge and national events.

Monitoring performance

Assessing your performance in an objective way will be difficult and simply using your finishing position can be unreliable. So to get a more comprehensive picture you may wish to assess your performance in five different ways:

1 Finishing position.

2 Your time behind the winner

3 Your time relative to the gold badge standard.

4 How much time you lost through mistakes.

5 How far you would have been behind the winner if you hadn't made any mistakes.

As you get fitter these should all improve and plotting each of them out on a graph is a good idea (see fig 2.2 (ii) opposite).

Don't expect a smooth graph; the vagaries of orienteering will prevent this and there will be some inconsistencies between your performance measures. Within a few months, however, you should see a general improvement.

Summary

● Competitive orienteering requires a specific form of fitness. This should be developed through a carefully constructed training programme, which applies the principles of training to the demands of the sport.

● Some forms of training may develop a single fitness component, others may develop a mixture. The correct balance must be attained within a whole programme if the correct form of fitness is to be achieved.

● Factors such as orienteering skills and psychological work can be incorporated into fitness training sessions, provided that they are not to the detriment of the fitness training work. Indeed, they may be used to provide added interest.

● Remember, if planning a session for others, that orienteers want to be out orienteering and circuit training may have little attraction unless they can see the relevance of the session.

● Training should be enjoyable – if it isn't then you or the orienteers that you coach are unlikely to stick with it. Even the best training programmes in the world are of no benefit if the individual doesn't actually do the sessions.

● Sometimes doing a session or an activity just for the fun of it is enough justification in itself. It will refresh the individual mentally and provide new interest, both of which are just as important as any fitness gains.

Chapter 2.3

Assessing Your Fitness

Fitness tests for orienteers - 3km time trial - terrain run - hill runs - obstacle agility run - summary

Fitness Tests for Orienteering

There are a number of reasons why you may wish to test your fitness. These include:

1. To evaluate your current level of fitness;

2. To monitor the effectiveness of your fitness training; and

3. To provide motivation for your training by using fitness tests as short term goals.

When conducting any form of fitness test it is important that the tests are specific to orienteering. In competitive orienteering you need to navigate between controls as rapidly as possible. This means that you have to run over a variety of terrains, ranging from flat paths to uneven ground covered with brashings. You must also be able to run up hills without undue fatigue and be sufficiently agile in your running to rapidly run through dense forest. These demands must be reflected in any fitness test, if it is to effectively assess your fitness for orienteering.

The fitness tests outlined in this section are designed to evaluate specific aspects of your orienteering fit-

ness. If undertaken at regular intervals (usually six to ten weeks) they can be used to monitor your fitness, thereby providing information on the effectiveness of a particular training schedule as well as acting as a form of motivation.

Since all the tests described require maximal exertion they should only be performed following an adequate warm up which includes five to ten minutes jogging, along with suitable stretching or loosening exercises.

The orienteering specific tests are:

1. 3km time trial.
2. Terrain run.
3. Hill runs.
4. Obstacle agility run.

Each test is in the form of a time trial conducted over orienteering type terrain and evaluates a different aspect of the fitness required to successfully compete in orienteering events. Since the results are based upon your actual performance they are simple to interpret. While these tests may not initially appear to be as impressive as laboratory based maximal oxygen uptake tests (VO_2 max.) or anaerobic

38

threshold tests (OBLA) they may be more relevant to you because of their specificity to the orienteering environment. That is not to say that sophisticated laboratory tests do not have their place in the world of sport science, but they do have their limitations, not least of all the lack of specificity. Running on a treadmill is not quite the same as running through rough, undulating forest.

Since the key fitness component required for orienteering is the ability to sustain a fast running pace, this is the central feature in all the tests. It is of course true that other fitness factors such as strength, anaerobic power and flexibility are also required in orienteering, but the reason we need them is to help us run

faster, so any improvements in these other areas should be reflected in your performance of the running tests.

As the tests are designed to be maximal, they should not be conducted on the same day. Often the most convenient way to do them is as part of a training session. When evaluating your results you need to remember that factors such as the weather; changes in the undergrowth; the conditions underfoot; fatigue from a previous day's training and simple daily variations may all have an influence upon your performance, so these things should be noted down with the test results.

Over a period of time you will collect a substantial amount of data for each of the assessments described here and hence have a good means of gauging your fitness. If carried out in a club setting the coach or training officer could collate the data to produce 'norms' and ratings for particular tests. This can help when interpreting the results of new members and be used to identify areas of their fitness which need particular attention.

Assessment 1 – 3km time trial

The purpose of this test is to assess your basic running fitness or endurance.

Orienteering events are prolonged and to complete them at speed requires a good basic level of aerobic fitness. Physiologically this type of fitness includes parameters such as your maximum capacity to utilise oxygen (aerobic capacity or VO_2 max.) and your ability to sustain a good running speed without accumulating too much of the fatigue inducing lactic acid. Whilst this latter factor can be specifi-

cally measured in the laboratory using complex 'Onset of Blood Lactate Accumulation' tests (OBLA) this aspect of fitness is automatically inherent within the performance test since it will affect how fast you can run the three kilometres.

Hence in this test your VO_2 max and OBLA are both being assessed indirectly through running speed which is after all what it is all about. Indeed, when you get down to basics, it is running speed around an orienteering course which counts and not who has the highest VO_2 max in the laboratory.

The 3km time trial should be run along paths or similar easy terrain. You should select a convenient location, and slight variations from the suggested 3km are not important. You may get the required distance by completing a set course or alternatively covering several laps of a shorter circuit.

Your performance is measured simply as the time you take to complete the distance. Since courses will vary in terms of their exact length, the terrain and the conditions underfoot, no definitive times are given here. It is up to you to collect your data over a period of time and to develop your own ratings and standards for the course. Always remember that the most important factor is the comparison between your current and previous times.

If training as a group the test should be run as a time trial rather than a race with each runner starting at 1 to 2 minute intervals, as this will more closely simulate an orienteering competition.

Assessment 2 – Terrain run

The purpose of this test is to evaluate your ability to run fast over rough and undulating ground.

You should select a suitable area of woodland or forest which includes some obstacles on the ground such as undergrowth or brashings; but it should still be runnable. You will need to mark out a course within this area using tape or cones. In the test you should run a course lasting between 2 and 3 minutes. Have a minute's recovery and then repeat the course twice more, again with a minute recovery in between. Add up the total time you took to complete the course three times.

In order to make valid comparisons at a later date you will need to carefully note the exact position of the course, including all obstacles and turning points.

Assessment 3 – Hill runs

Since hills are an integral part of most orienteering events, the ability to run up hills is an important fitness requirement. This particular fitness test will assess your leg strength and anaerobic endurance for this type of running.

For the test you should select a relatively long hill that is not too steep and with a route that is reasonable underfoot, making it runnable. The length of the hill should be such that it takes between 1 and 3 minutes to run up. As with the other tests, you should run up the hill as fast as possible, recording your time for the ascent. You should then jog down to the bottom of the hill taking about twice as much time. This is your re-

covery. Repeat this 3 to 6 times and then add up the total amount of time taken for the ascents. If you can you should be fairly precise with the amount of recovery time you give yourself.

When you come to repeat the test at a later date you must use the same hill, the same number of repetitions and the same amount of recovery. If you change any of these factors then the comparisons become less meaningful.

Assessment 4 – Obstacle/agility run

The purpose of this assessment is to evaluate your running ability over varied terrain and cope with changes of pace, negotiating obstacles and changing direction.

You should select an area of varied undulating terrain which includes a number of obstacles such as fallen trees which need to be jumped and tight bends as you zig-zag between trees. A circuit which takes 2 to 3 minutes is recommended so it should be about 400-600 metres in length.

Record your time taken to complete the distance, have a minute's rest and repeat the run twice more. Add up your total time for the three runs. For future comparisons you will need to note the exact route of the course.

Summary

● If used correctly, fitness tests can provide you with important information about your level of fitness and how well your training is going. They can also help you to identify any specific weakness in your running. For example when compared to your club mates you may do well in the 3km time trial but struggle on the obstacle agility run. This will tell you what you need to work on in your training.

● The distances and number of repetitions suggested for each of these tests are just guidelines. The important points are the specificity of the tests.

● In some cases you may prefer to design a course consisting of several laps rather than just one. Provided you apply the general principles the exact distance and number of repetitions are not important.

● In order to make valid comparisons it will be important to replicate the course exactly in any subsequent tests.

PART THREE

Training Routines & Techniques

Chapter 3.1
Training Ingredients

Now that you have worked out which aspects of your fitness you want to improve and how you should plan your training, you will need to decide the details of what goes into your training programme.

This part outlines several different forms of training and gives examples of a number of suitable exercises which you could incorporate into a personal training programme. When constructing your programme, always refer back to the principles of training, think what it is you are trying to get out of the training and whether your programme is likely to achieve these aims.

As an orienteer your most important fitness training will involve running. The section on running fitness training gives some suggested variations which you might like to try. In addition to this you can supplement your running with some strengthen-

ing exercises. These will be beneficial if your leg, abdominal or upper body muscles lack the strength you need.

Flexibility is another area of fitness which many orienteers could benefit from. For example, you may find that by improving your suppleness you will run more fluently. Try it and see.

Plan your training carefully. Doing a bit of this and a bit of that in a random fashion will not be as effective as systematically setting out a clear programme which includes all the important elements that you need and progresses logically from your current level of fitness to your intended peak.

Whatever training you do, remember to include some form of warm up. Attempting to exercise strenuously without preparing your body for the exertion can be a shock to the system. So always start off gently with a few minutes loosening exercises and easy jogging.

Chapter 3.2

Warming Up

Why warm up?- what to do - how much to do stretching - lessening the risk of injury - a basic warm up routine - a note on warming down - summary

Why Warm Up?

There are many misconceptions about what a warm up is, what it should include and what benefits can be gained from warming up. In fact there are four good reasons why everyone should warm up before any form of strenuous exercise:

1. It can improve performance.
2. It helps prevent injury.
3. It prevents undue stress being put on the heart.
4. It can help to prepare you mentally for the event.

What to Do

For the orienteer a warm up should begin with some gentle loosening exercises followed by a few minutes jogging at a comfortable pace. This will increase the flow of blood to the exercising muscles by:

1. Increasing the heart rate.
2. Opening up the blood vessels in the muscles.
3. Diverting blood from areas such as the gut.

These responses will last for several minutes after the warm up has ceased and have the effect of increasing the supply of oxygen to the muscles. This makes the onset of exercise seem easier and prevents premature fatigue occurring in the early stages of the run. Failing to warm up can cause an inadequate supply of oxygen to the muscles, resulting in an unnecessary build up of lactic acid felt as a burning, aching sensation in the legs even at relatively slow speeds.

Gentle jogging will also increase the temperature of the muscles, enabling the energy releasing reactions to occur faster and making the muscle fluids less viscous. The muscles can then contract faster against less internal resistance, thereby making running easier.

Co-ordination and balance can also be improved by warming up (an important aspect if starting out over rough terrain).

How Much to Do

How much jogging you do in the warm up will depend on the weather, how you feel on the day and, quite simply, some individuals prefer to do more than others. Find out what suits you, but as a general guideline, it should be sufficient to induce a slight sweat. So on cold days wear additional clothing whilst warming up.

The best way to warm up for an event is on the way to the start, so don't complain about the 1 - 1.5k distance from the assembly area - make good use of it.

Stretching

The jogging part of a warm up should be followed by some stretching exercises. Muscles are less prone to injury if properly warmed up and stretched. Stretching exercises will also increase your ability to move more easily and freely, as the muscles will offer less resistance to the movement.

The type of stretching you do is also very important. All too often, people are observed doing a bouncing action (ballistic stretching). In a sport such as orienteering this is unnecessary and should be avoided. It is not the best way to stretch the muscles, and can actually cause injuries.

The reason for not bouncing is because of the muscle's stretch reflex. If a muscle is stretched rapidly the stretch is detected by sensors in the muscles (proprioceptors). These cause the muscle to respond by automatically contracting. If it is still being stretched against this contraction (as occurs when bouncing), the conflict can result in a pulled muscle or tendon.

At this point it is important to distinguish between controlled loosening exercises and forced ballistic stretches. The former describes a controlled movement, performed within the joint's normal range, whereas the latter is a forced ballistic action which can cause injury. Muscles and tendons should always be stretched slowly and gently without a bouncing action. They should be gently stretched to the point of slight discomfort but not pain and then the stretched position held for at least 10 seconds. This has been demonstrated to be the most effective form of stretching and is referred to as static stretching. Gentle static stretching avoids the dramatic reflex contraction and thus gives a more effective form of stretching without the risk of injury.

Lessening the Risk of Injury

It is a mistake to think that injuries only happen to fast runners or when the terrain is particularly hazardous. A slight stumble whilst jogging across undulating parkland may be enough to cause a pulled hamstring muscle or a strained Achilles tendon. It could be that one isolated incident which ruins your season.

Performing an appropriate warm up may be just sufficient to lessen the extent of such injuries or even prevent them in some cases. By adhering to the guidelines presented in the next section you should increase your chances of an injury free year and minimise the extent of any injury you might acquire.

In addition to these benefits there is a further reason for warming up. It has been shown that in a great proportion of 'normal' people, doing strenuous exercise without a prior warm up causes irregular electrical activity in the heart (cardiac arhythmia). If a suitable warm up is undertaken before the strenuous exercise, this irregularity is greatly reduced or absent.

Finally, many performers find that

a warm up is an essential part of their pre-event routine. It provides a familiar sequence of activities which enables them to prepare mentally and gets them into the right frame of mind for the training session or competition.

A Basic Warm Up Routine

A pre-exercise warm up routine should consist of the following phases:

1. General loosening.
2. Walking and/or jogging.
3. Static stretching.

The physical demands of orienteering require that the emphasis of the pre-exercise routine be upon preparing the cardiovascular system and legs for the activity. The exercises illustrated in this routine have been selected for their effectiveness and convenience. For example, some authorities may prefer a seated hamstring stretch to the standing version mentioned here. However, it is not always the most convenient to perform in a cold, wet, muddy field.

Warm Up Phase 1 – Gentle Loosening

This phase concentrates upon gradually mobilising the joints and gently getting the muscles working. This is especially important if it is cold or you have been sat in the car for sometime whilst driving to the event. All the loosening exercises presented in this section should be performed in a slow, controlled manner at a rate of about one repetition a second. All rotation movements should be repeated about 6 - 10 times in both directions, with the emphasis of each exercise being on gently easing the joint through its maximum range of movement.

Warm Up Phase 1 - Gentle Loosening

1. Ankle rotations

In a seated or standing position slowly circle one foot in a clockwise direction. Repeat the movement in the opposite direction. Repeat the process using the other leg.

2. Heel raises

Stand with your feet approximately shoulder width apart. Then alternately raise and lower your heels off the ground whilst keeping both feet in contact with the ground. This will produce a gentle jogging motion that should be gradually increased until you are lifting each foot off of the ground and are jogging on the spot. This exercise should be performed for at least 30 seconds.

3. Hip rotations

Stand on one leg holding onto a sup-port for balance. Slowly rotate the raised leg by moving the knee to-wards the mid-line of the body and then away in a large circular move-ment. Repeat in both directions and on both legs.

4. Spinal rotations

Stand with your feet approximately shoulder width apart. Then slowly rotate your upper body in a circular motion. Repeat in both directions.

Warm Up Phase 2 – Walking and Jogging

The aim of this phase is to elevate the heart rate, increase blood flow to the muscles and raise the temperature of the muscles, tendons and joints.

In most events this will be an inevitable activity on the way to the start and whether you choose to walk or jog will depend upon your level of fitness and how vigorously you intend to go round the course.

However, don't forget to include it as part of a training session, when you should ensure that the first 5 - 10 minutes are at an easy pace below your normal training speed. Even if going off on a steady run, you should start off at a walk or very gentle jog and gradually increase your speed up to your full training pace over the first few minutes.

Warm Up Phase 3 – Static Stretching

Aim to get to the start of an event with a few minutes to spare so that you can complete this final phase of the warm up before you start.

Alternatively, if you are out on a training run pause for a few minutes when you feel warmed up and do some stretching before you increase the pace again.

This is particularly important if you are intending to do interval training or hill repetitions which will place additional stress on the muscles. If you are doing a steady run then either do the stretching early on in the run or after you get back as a means of maintaining your flexibility and helping you to cool down.

The aim of the stretching phase of the warm up is to gently stretch out the muscles and connective tissue. This will help to remove any residual tightness and reduce the risk of damage, if and when they are vigorously stretched during the event. All stretched positions should be reached slowly without jerking and then held for at least 10 seconds.

When doing these exercises you should feel a comfortable stretch in the muscles. You should not stretch to the point of pain. Jerking or bouncing movements whilst stretching will cause the muscle fibres to tense up and reduce the effectiveness of the stretch. They can also increase the risk of injury by forcing the muscles beyond their natural length.

Warm Up Phase 3 – Static Stretching

1. Calf stretch

Using a tree or fence for support, take a step back with one foot. Gently lower the heal of your back leg onto the ground and straighten the knee.

This should produce a slight stretch in the muscles of the calf (mainly the gastrocnemius). If it does not then try moving the back leg further back and tilting the hips forwards. Hold the stretch for the desired duration and repeat on both legs.

2. Calf and Achilles stretch

This is similar to the previous stretch, but in this case the knee of the back leg should be slightly bent. Again both feet should be kept flat on the ground. This should produce a slight stretch in the soleus muscle of the calf and in the Achilles tendon at the base of the calf.

3. Inner thigh (adductor) stretch

Stand with your feet approximately 18 inches wider than shoulder width apart. Turn one foot out so that it is facing to the side whilst the other faces forwards. Whilst keeping both feet flat on the ground bend the knee of the sideways facing foot. This will lower the body to one side. Keeping the other knee straight will cause a slight amount of stretch down the inner thigh.

Warm Up Phase 3
— Static Stretching

4. Hip flexor stretch

Kneel on one knee and move the hips forward slowly until stretch is felt in the front thigh of the back leg. Try to keep the front knee over the front foot.

5. Hamstring stretch

Place one foot on an elevated object such as a convenient knoll or root-stock. Then, keeping the knee of the elevated leg straight, place your hands on the thigh of the elevated leg and gently move them towards your ankle.

Whilst doing this, try to keep your back straight. If you feel a strain in the back it means that you are doing it incorrectly. In this case, you should try it again ensuring that you bend from the waist. If a strain is felt behind the knee, you should bend it slightly so that the stretch is felt within the muscle.

As an alternative hamstring stretch, kneel on one knee with the other leg extended in front of you. Then gently reach down towards the ankle as before, to achieve the stretched position.

6. Quadriceps stretch

Using a support for balance, stand on one leg. Bend the knee of the other leg, bringing the foot up behind you, and grasp the ankle with one hand. Hold the foot close to the buttock making sure that the knee is in the correct alignment and not twisted. This should produce a slight stretch down the front of the thigh. Further stretch may be produced by leaning forward slightly.

A note on warming down

Strenuous exercise causes the production of numerous metabolic waste products which the body needs to flush out of the muscles and dispose of.

A gentle jog followed by some easy stretching can assist with this process and also helps to gradually return the body to its resting state. Many orienteers find it useful in reducing the likelihood of muscular stiffness the following day. This is an important consideration in multi-day events.

Take advantage of the route back to the car park for an easy jog. Do some gentle stretching by the drinks or while you discuss the course with fellow competitors.

Summary

● Warming up before training or an event should not only improve your performance, but may also prevent the occurrence of unnecessary injury. There may be a high price to pay if you don't warm up. Injury could force you to miss a few weeks or even retire from the sport.

● Warming up can easily be done by jogging gently on the way to the start and stretching as you wait for your start time. It is not a waste of energy - in the long term it may be the most important few minutes of exercise you do that day.

Chapter 3.3
Running training

Introduction - types of running training – steady running – intensive repetitions – hill training – interval training – fartlek – paarlauf – running training in the periodised year – the conditioning phase – intensive sport specific phase – competition phase – recovery phase - summary

Introduction

The amount of 'training' undertaken by orienteers varies considerably, from those who do virtually nothing, to those who train nearly every day. For any orienteer, running is the most vital part of their training, as it will provide them with the essential foundation of aerobic fitness, stamina and endurance.

There are different types of running training which can be included into a training programme. They differ in their intensity and duration, and as a consequence, will have slightly different training effects on the body. An outline of these types of training is given below and this is followed by some guidelines of how to incorporate them into your training year.

Regardless of the type of training, a warm up should always be included. Even if just going out for a steady run, ensure that you loosen up before you start and that the first few minutes of the run are completed at an easy jog.

If you are doing a more strenuous session this period of jogging should be increased up to 10 minutes

and then followed by some stretching before you start the intensive efforts. If you have a set venue for your hill sessions or interval work the warm up is likely to be completed as you jog out to the venue.

At the end of each session a short cool down period should also be included. Typically this will involve a few minutes gentle jogging on the way back from your hill or interval session, or alternatively by ensuring that you end your steady run with a few minutes of easy jogging and not a sprint finish. This should be followed by some easy stretching before you shower and get changed.

Types of running training

Running for orienteering can be divided into two broad categories:
1. Steady Running.
2. Intensive repetition running: this includes interval training, hill repetitions, fartlek and paarlauf relays.

In both categories of running training the principles of training apply. That is to say that an improvement in fitness is caused by overloading the body, which causes it to make

positive adaptations to these stresses.

In steady state running the heart rate, cardio-respiratory and aerobic pathways in the muscles are made to work harder than they do at rest. The activity occurs for a prolonged period of time (30 - 120 minutes) and at an intensity of between 65 and 85% of the individual's aerobic capacity. This promotes certain improvements in fitness.

Once an individual is relatively fit, additional benefits may be gained from utilising more intensive forms of training once or twice a week. However, the demands of such training limit its use to fitter individuals and, even then, recovery days will be needed between the intensive sessions, usually in the form of steady running.

Whatever running you do, try

not to forget the importance of specificity and the need to spend some time off the paths running across other terrain.

Steady running

Steady running is the most fundamental of all types of running training and it will form the basis of most orienteers' training programmes. It involves completing a set distance at a fairly consistent pace.

Provided it is undertaken at the correct intensity, duration and frequency, this type of training will provide an individual with a foundation of aerobic fitness and muscular endurance. It increases the body's capacity to utilise oxygen and the improvements in fitness result in the orienteer being able to sustain a faster running pace over prolonged distances.

There is some debate over the exact nature of steady state running and the relative merits of running at particular intensities. Some authorities advocate running for long distances at a comfortable speed, a training technique known as 'Long, Slow Distance' or LSD. Others recommend running at much faster speeds, typically just below an individual's anaerobic threshold, but for shorter distances. In both cases the run is completed at a fairly consistent speed.

It is up to individuals to discover what suits them – long duration or high intensity – and which they prefer. A combination of the two may be the answer.

Intensive repetition running

Many orienteers will utilise steady running as their sole form of training and it may be quite adequate for the level of fitness they wish to attain. If, however, a higher level of fitness is desired then some of the more intensive forms of training should be considered. These forms of training are used once a basic foundation of aerobic fitness has been established via steady running.

Intensive repetition training involves periods of work, such as running uphill, followed by phases of more gentle exercise, such as jogging back down the hill, as a means of recovery. During the phase of intensive running, greater demands are placed upon the cardiovascular system and muscles as they are forced to work at and beyond their capacity to utilise oxygen. This results in the accumulation of lactic acid and the fatiguing sensation in the muscles.

Such overload on the body is of far greater intensity than that encountered in a steady run. For example your heart rate will get close to its maximum, which it does not do in a steady run. Therefore, by repeatedly elevating your heart rate to this level and making your body work at this intensity, a far greater overload and training effect is experienced.

The same rationale also applies to the other factors which influence an orienteer's aerobic capacity, such as the muscles' capacity to extract and utilise oxygen. These too will be made to work at their maximal rate.

Due to its intensity and the additional stresses placed upon the body, intensive repetition work should be phased in gradually. For example, attempting to do 20 x 400m hill runs as your first intensive session is likely to be a shock to your body. It may even cause injuries, especially to the Achilles tendon, which will not have been used to that level of exertion.

Start with five repetitions the first time and include them within a steady run. Increase the number gradually over a period of weeks, remembering to apply the principle of progression in your training.

There are various forms of intensive repetition training, these include hill sessions, intervals, fartlek and paarlauf relays.

Hill training

Hill repetitions involve running hard uphill, followed by a brief recovery as you jog back down to the bottom of the hill. The length of the hill may be anything from less than 100m to over 400m, depending upon what is available to you.

The session should commence with about 10 minutes jogging, followed by some stretching and a few short efforts up the lower slopes of the hill. The number and duration of your repetitions will vary according to your fitness, but in total should last between 20 and 40 minutes. So a typical session could be 12 x a 300m hill. This will then be followed by a 10 minute jog as a cool down.

Hill training will also help to provide you with the muscular strength and anaerobic power needed to run powerfully uphill during an event. But be careful of your achilles tendon, which may be overstressed if you attempt to do too much too soon.

Interval Training

Interval training involves repeatedly running a set distance or time, with a set period of recovery. Typically these distances may be between 1 and 2 minutes duration with a similar period of recovery. As you get fitter the recovery phase can be reduced to about half the duration of the effort.

Initial sessions may be made up of a 10 minute warm up jog followed by some stretching and 6 x 2 minute efforts with 90 seconds recovery.

For the really fit this may be increased to something like 12 x 2 minute efforts with 60 seconds recovery. For this kind of session a stopwatch with a count down mode is useful. If possible the session should be conducted in orienteering type terrain and getting off the paths for at least some of the efforts will make the training more specific to what you experience in an orienteering event. The session should be completed with the usual 10 minute jog cool down.

Fartlek training

Fartlek means 'speed game' and is a less formal type of interval training. There are a number of variations on this form of training, but in general it should be undertaken in orienteering type terrain and be more or less 'do as you please'.

This means that once you have warmed up you may run hard to a tree in the distance, then jog until you feel like striding up the next hill, and so on for the duration of the session. Some other exercises such as sit ups and press ups may also be incorporated into the session at will.

Paarlauf relays

Paarlauf relays are a good way of interval training as a group. The problem with many forms of interval training is that the less fit get left behind and get less recovery. With paarlauf relays a group is divided into teams of twos or

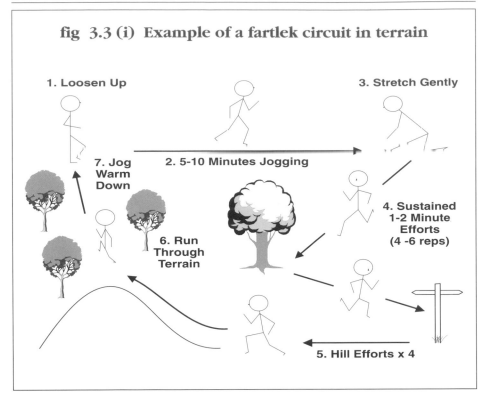

fig 3.3 (i) Example of a fartlek circuit in terrain

1. Loosen Up

2. 5-10 Minutes Jogging

3. Stretch Gently

4. Sustained 1-2 Minute Efforts (4 -6 reps)

5. Hill Efforts x 4

6. Run Through Terrain

7. Jog Warm Down

threes, with the teams being as evenly matched as possible. A circuit is marked out and the first member of each team runs it. This runner then hands over to the next team member who runs it hands over to the next member. If working in teams of two this will be the first team member, who will run the lap again. This goes on continuously for a set period of time, which may be 15 to 30 minutes. It is a form of interval training but one in which the group is kept together and everyone can run at his or her own pace.

There are a number of variations on this theme. For example, the group can be divided into two, with all the fitter runners being placed in one group and the less fit in the other. Within each of these subgroups the

runners are ranked and this will determine the sequence in which they set off at each change over.

The 'fast ' group sets off round the course. As the group comes in the first runner hands over to the slowest ranked runner in the second group, the second runner in hands over to the second slowest and so on. When the 'slow' group complete their lap and come into change over the first one in hands over to the slowest runner of the fast group, the next one hands over to the next slowest and so on, so that the fastest runner in the group always goes off last. This is repeated for the set duration of the relay. It is organised so that the slowest runner in each group goes off first and the fastest runner in each group goes off last. This helps to keep the group together. There are no actual teams as the change over is determined by the finishing sequence of the group.

Alternatively the runners may pair up to form as equal teams as possible. So the fastest and slowest runners will form one team, the second fastest and second slowest another, and so on.

They will then run the course as a continuous relay as described above, but will always hand over to the same person. This makes the training a little more competitive.

Running training in the periodised year

For some individuals running training will consist solely of doing two or three steady runs a week, which they will then continue to do throughout the year. Many orienteers find that this type of consistent training gives them the level of fitness they need. Others prefer an annual training programme which is divided into phases. In this case, you will need to divide the orienteering year into four:

1. General conditioning
2. Intensive sport specific
3. Competition
4. Recovery

This was discussed in chapter 2.1.

General conditioning

In orienteering in Britain the general conditioning phase would occur in the autumn and early winter months. It involves the development of a foun-

Fig 3.3 (ii) Example of a periodised year's training

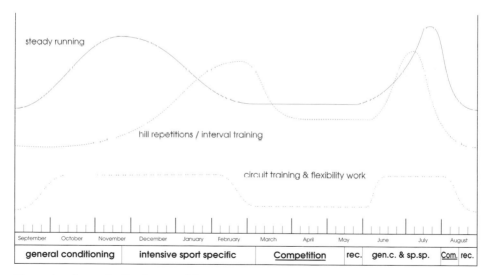

Example of a periodised year with two competition phases. The build-up to the second competition phase is foreshortened, but the individual will still possess a basic level of fitness from the spring. Competition phases are followed by recovery.

dation of aerobic fitness through running a high mileage. This mileage must be increased gradually during this phase to enable your body to adapt to the demands being made of it. This is because any form of training will put certain stresses upon your body. These stresses normally act as stimuli, which your body responds to by making the necessary physiological adaptations that will improve fitness.

However, if the amount of training is considerably more than you are used to then the stresses may be more than your body can cope with. This will mean that, rather than improving your fitness, you will become worn out and fatigued. This can result in those unwanted aches and pains that can develop into overuse injuries.

So when increasing mileage, do it gradually and in a planned manner over a period of weeks.

Intensive sport specific

Typically the intensive sport specific phase occurs early in the new year. In this more demanding phase you aim to sharpen up your fitness. The volume of training is reduced by decreasing the number of miles run each week, but the intensity of the training increases by including sessions of hill repetitions and fartlek in place of a couple of the steady runs.

Competition

The competition phase should coincide with your most important events. It is when the amount of training is reduced in both volume and intensity. This ensures that you are fresh for the major events. In some cases training may be nearly halved and certainly should be in the week before a key event.

Recovery

After a hard season your body will need some time to recuperate and recover. This is achieved by a few weeks rest or just very light training. In many sports this phase coincides with a holiday. However in orienteering this is often not the case since for many orienteers a holiday means the Welsh or Scottish 6 day, the Lakeland 5 day and the White Rose. Hardly the relaxing, restful occasions which most people associate with a holiday!

Planning an orienteering programme in this way can be difficult as the sport goes on throughout the year, but it is still possible to identify the most important events for you and alter the emphasis of the training at different times of the year in order to achieve a periodising effect, enabling you to peak when it really counts.

Chapter 3.4

Strength Training

Introduction - before you start - how much to do - repetitions and sets - exercising at home - circuit training - strengthening exercises - leg exercises - upper body exercises - abdominal exercises - safety considerations

Introduction

In orienteering the most obvious fitness requirement is the ability to run. Therefore much of an orienteer's training should be centred upon running. However, in orienteering there are other less obvious fitness requirements which are also very important. If all you do is run, then you may be neglecting these other aspects of your fitness, which can actually help your running.

Many orienteers, for instance, could benefit from basic strengthening and conditioning exercises. This doesn't mean that orienteers need to develop their muscles to look like those of body-builders, but that they could benefit from some improvements in the general condition of their musculature.

Indeed, most orienteers completely ignore the training of the muscles in their arms, shoulders and abdominal region, perhaps because the importance of these muscles in a sport like orienteering is not obvious at first. If you have abdominal and shoulder muscles that are in poor condition they are more likely to fatigue during the later stages of an event, causing your body to sag and making running more difficult. You may have experienced this when running over difficult terrain. Upper body strength is also an asset when hauling yourself up a steep slope or climbing out of a deep gully.

As for leg strength, whilst running will obviously strengthen the leg muscles, additional leg exercises can help, especially for running uphill, through mud, or over uneven ground.

Therefore for a comprehensive level of orienteering fitness you need to supplement your running with a few extra exercises that will strengthen the body parts other routines cannot reach.

The exercises described here may be performed on an individual basis or as a circuit. Often the latter can be the most convenient arrangement, especially if training in a group.

The exercises are selected to help you tone up weak or sagging muscles. By performing them on a regular basis you may see as well as feel the benefit. By performing these exercises you are not going to dramatically increase the size of your muscles but you will improve the condition of what you have already got. Anyone who is concerned about 'bulking up' need not worry. It is a misconception that all strengthening exercises will greatly increase the size of your muscles. In reality you have to do a lot of training with heavy weights before you increase the size of your muscles to any great extent. This is especially so for women who possess lower levels of the anabolic hormones.

The aim of these exercises is to increase the strength and endurance of your muscles by improving their quality rather than by increasing their size.

Before you start

Remember to warm up before you start. As with all forms of training you should gradually prepare the body for any strenuous physical exertion. Cold muscles are more vulnerable to strain, so a good time to do your strengthening exercises may be in the few minutes after a run when your muscles will be fully warmed up.

However, this may not be practical or you may choose to do your strengthening exercises at another time. If you do then be careful and don't rush into them even if you are in a hurry. Doing sit ups and press ups first thing in the morning when you've just got out of bed may appear to be commendable, but if your body isn't ready you could strain yourself. Spend a few extra minutes gradually loosening up the body and promoting the circulation before you start.

You can do this by walking and then jogging on the spot for a few minutes before performing the loosening exercises described in the section on warming up. This should ensure that your muscles are ready to be worked and you will get the most out of the exercises.

How much to do

Due to the wide range in the ages and fitness levels of orienteers, it is not possible to prescribe a specific number of repetitions for each exercise described here. There are, however, certain guidelines you can use to help you decide what is right for you.

Firstly, if you are unfamiliar with an exercise then start with just a few repetitions. Don't push yourself beyond your limits, as you may strain the muscles. Remember, just because you run regularly, it doesn't necessarily mean that you will be able to do a large number of sit ups.

If your muscles are stiff the day after the exercises then you should reduce the number until you find a level that your muscles can cope with. Then you can gradually increase the number as your muscles get stronger and more able to cope with the exercises.

These strengthening exercises can be done almost every day although most people will find that they can benefit from 3 - 5 times a week. Once or twice a week will certainly be better than nothing at all. However as a cautionary note, *'IF IT HURTS, DON'T DO IT'!* Forget about the 'no pain, no gain' syndrome; that is the route to injury.

Whilst you may have to sometimes push yourself in training in order to improve your fitness, there is a subtle difference between the slight discomfort caused through training hard and the pain caused by overtraining. In all forms of training, listen to your body. Be sensible and don't exceed your limits. If you overdo it during the first few sessions, you will only make your muscles sore and have to rest them for a few days.

Repetitions and sets

When you first start a new exercise try between 10 and 15 repetitions. You may stick at this or alternatively you may build up to 30 - 50 repetitions, depending upon your desired level of fitness. This number of continuous repetitions is referred to as a set.

When you are familiar with an exercise and have established how many repetitions you can do in one set you can then progress further by doing two or three sets of the same exercise. The second set of a particular exercise may be performed directly after the first (with a short rest in between) or you may complete one set of all your exercises before repeating them all again. This way the muscles have more time to recover.

A typical session could therefore look like this:
1. Sit ups (30 reps)
2. Single leg mini squats: heel flat (10 reps each leg)
3. Press ups or elevated press ups (15 reps)
4. Twisted sit ups (20 reps)
5. Single leg mini squats: heel raised (10 reps each leg)
6. Dips (20 reps)
7. Abdominal crunches (10 reps)
8. Step ups (30 reps)
9. Running arms (30 reps)
Complete all 9 exercises then repeat. Remember, no matter what your fitness,

to warm up before you start. Start with a number of repetitions you can easily attain and progress gradually.

Exercising at home

Many of the exercises mentioned here can be performed at home without the use of specialist apparatus. There are of course numerous variations on the exercises with which you may be familiar or which you may prefer if you have the facilities available.

Circuit training

Circuit training provides a sociable form of training which if organised appropriately can be used to improve aerobic fitness, endurance and strength.

A circuit normally consists of 9 - 12 exercises performed in a set order. Typically the circuit can then be repeated two or three times. Depending upon the circumstances and resources available, the circuit may be organised in a number of ways. Factors to consider include:

(i) *The Room* – Ideally circuit training would take place in a gym or sports hall, but almost any venue can be used.

When setting out the exercise area, safety is important and the exercise stations should be positioned so as to minimise the risk of collisions when moving between exercises. The best way to ensure this is to position the stations so that the participants move around the room in one direction without their paths crossing.

(ii) *The Duration or Repetition of Each Exercise* – The amount of each exercise performed can be determined either by giving the participants a certain number of repetitions to complete

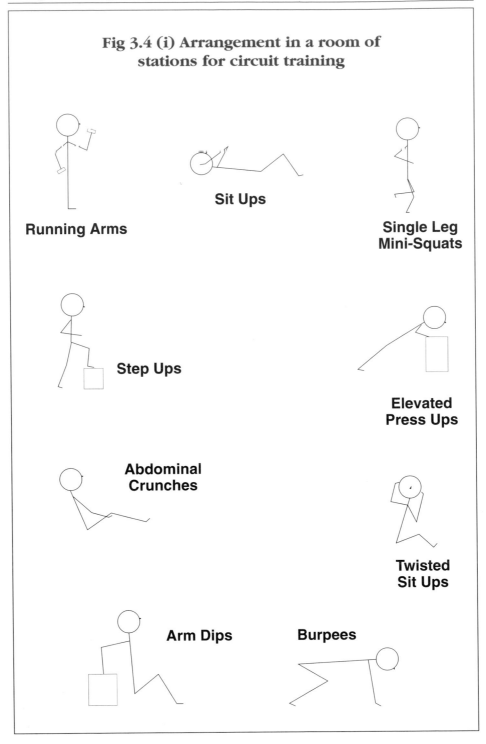

Fig 3.4 (i) Arrangement in a room of stations for circuit training

Running Arms

Sit Ups

Single Leg Mini-Squats

Step Ups

Elevated Press Ups

Abdominal Crunches

Twisted Sit Ups

Arm Dips

Burpees

or by getting them to complete as many repetitions as they can within a set time. Regardless of which method is used, it is important that the quality of the exercises are retained even when trying to perform them rapidly.

If working to a set number of repetitions each participant may have a different number for each exercise. This will be determined by their level of fitness and ability to perform each exercise. In order to do this each participant should have a written programme stating the number of repetitions. They could then time themselves to see how long it takes them to complete the session. The time should come down as they get fitter, allowing the number of repetitions to be gradually increased.

Alternatively, if the participants are to work for a set time duration, such as 30 seconds, they should again keep a record of how many repetitions they achieve of each exercise. With this method, it is usual to give a similar time interval of thirty seconds recovery between exercises. Watches with a countdown facility are useful for this form of training.

One of the easiest ways to organise a group circuit session is to get all the participants to start together, each commencing at a different exercise station. The session leader then calls out when to start, stop and change exercise stations. In this way, the group works and finishes together. It also prevents queuing for a particular station.

(iii) *Recovery between Exercises* – To some extent recovery is inherent within the design of the circuit as alternate groups of muscles are worked and then rested.

If the participants are attempting to complete the circuit as fast as possible, they will dictate their own recovery. Alternatively, if the group is working for a set time at each exercise then the leader can specify a set time for recovery as they move between exercise stations. This may be anything between 20 - 40 seconds.

The recovery itself could be passive (simply walking between stations) or active with the participants jogging once or twice around the room between exercises. This will keep the heart rate up and give the session an element of aerobic training.

(iv) *Progression* – As the fitness of participants improves, the circuit will need to be adapted. To produce progression, you can increase the number of repetitions completed of each exercise, or the duration can be increased from 30 to 40 seconds, with a possible decrease in the time allowed for recovery. You can also increase the number (variety) of exercises within each circuit or the number of times the circuit is completed within each session.

(v) *Personal records* – Each individual should keep a record of each session noting the number of repetitions achieved and/or the time needed to complete the circuit.

This provides a record of their progression and indicates when the circuit needs to be modified in accordance with improving level of fitness. Such records can also be used to set fitness goals and provide motivation.

(vi) *Timing and Organisation* – If training as a group, it is usual for all members to warm up together and then start the circuit at the same time. If this is not possible due to participants arriving at different times, then the coach may set out the exercise stations and the participants start individually once they have warmed up and are ready.

Strengthening Exercises

The exercises described here are divided into three types:

1. leg exercises
2. upper body exercises
3. abdominal exercises.

For the abdominal exercises you should use a mat to protect your back, which can be made sore if you attempt the exercises on a hard surface. Small exercise mats can be bought at most sports shops, but as an alternative to a mat, several folded towels or a duvet can be used as a temporary substitute.

The exercises should normally be completed in a sequence which alternately works and then rests the different muscle groups. So the order could be legs, abdominal, upper body, legs, abdominal, upper body, etc. Some of the exercises will of course involve more than one group. For instance, whilst press ups obviously use the arm and shoulder muscles, they also use the abdominal muscles which hold the body in position. If you don't believe it then try doing press ups immediately after a hard set of sit ups. Find a sequence that suits you.

Leg exercises

1. Single leg mini squats: heel flat and heel raised

Stand on one leg with your foot flat on the floor. Slowly lower yourself down a few inches by slightly bending the knee (keep looking straight ahead and don't bend your back). Don't go down too far, or you won't be able to get back up again and you don't want to put unwanted stress on your knees. Raise yourself up by straightening your knee to return to the starting position.

This exercise will strengthen the leg muscles, including those which stabilise your leg, thus helping your balance when running over rough ground. Perform the exercise the desired

number of times and then repeat it using the other leg. Remember to control the movement, it may be more difficult than it sounds.

When you are able to cope with this version of the exercise, you may like to vary it by raising the heel off the ground each time you straighten your leg, so that you are on the ball of the foot. This makes the exercise more difficult, as it requires greater leg strength and balance.

2. *Step ups*

There are a number of variations of the step up. Some are done as fast as possible on a low step whilst others are performed more slowly using a relatively high step for leg strength. You will have to make your own decision on this, depending upon the steps you have available. The one I describe here is for strengthening the muscles at the front of the thigh, which often fatigue when you run uphill. It also simulates the kind of movement you

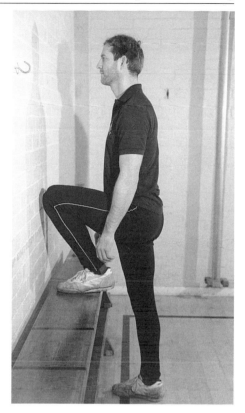

might do when climbing out of a steep gully or up a rocky outcrop.

Use a step which is about the same height as your knee. You may use two steps but make sure that whatever you use is stable and won't topple over. Putting the step against a wall is the usual arrangement.

Place your right foot on the step whilst your left remains on the ground. This is the starting position. Then bring your left foot onto the step so that both feet are on the step and extend both knees so that you stand up

straight. Lower your right foot onto the ground whilst keeping your left on the step. Then place your right leg back on the step and stand up straight before lowering your left foot onto the ground. Repeat this sequence.

You should always have one foot on the step and this will alternate between your right and left foot with each step. Use your thigh muscles to lift yourself up onto the step. Start steadily, increasing the speed as you become more familiar with the exercise.

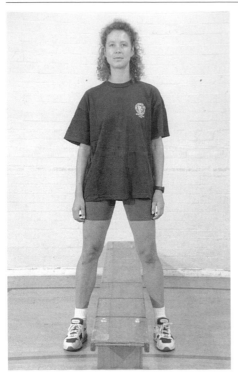

3. Astride jumps (left)

Stand with your feet either side of a bench. Jump onto the bench with both feet and then immediately jump off, back into the starting position. Repeat this as rapidly as possible.

4. Ski jumps (right)

For this you will need either a bench or two parallel lines approximately 18" apart. Stand on one side of the bench (or lines) facing along its length. Jump sideways over the bench (or lines) and then immediately jump back. Repeat this as rapidly as possible

5. Burpees (below right)

Start in the press up position. Quickly bring your feet forwards towards your hands and then back again. This should be repeated rapidly. To make it more difficult, you can put in a vertical jump. This is done each time you bring your feet up to your hands before you return them to the starting position.

As an alternative to the first version, you can commence the exercise with one leg bent so that the foot is up by your hands whilst the other is extended. You then rapidly move the extended leg forward while the other is moved back. This is repeated rapidly in a form of running action

Ski Jumps

Burpees

Upper body exercises

1. Press ups / Elevated press ups

Lie face down, placing your hands on the floor slightly wider than shoulder width apart, with the fingers pointing forwards. Straighten your arms so that you are balancing on your hands and feet, this is the starting position.

Bend your arms to lower your body down so that your face almost touches the floor. When you do this try to keep your back straight and do not let it sag in the middle. Also make sure that you are lowering your body rather than just nodding your head! Straighten your arms so that you raise your body back into the starting position.

The full press up is quite difficult. As an alternative you could try an easier version which involves exactly the same movement, but with your hands placed on an elevated surface such as a bench, stairs or kitchen work surface.

This elevates the upper body making the exercise easier: the higher the starting position the easier the exercise. As you get stronger you will need to look for lower bits of furniture upon which to exercise.

2. Arm dips

These can be done using a bench, stable chair, stairs or even the side of the bath. Place your hands behind with your fingers pointing forwards. Position your legs so that they are extending out in front of you and your weight is balanced between your hands and feet. Lower your body by bending your arms so that they bend to about 90 at the elbow. Straighten your arms to lift yourself back up again.

Repeat the exercise for as many repetitions as you wish. To make it more difficult, you can try elevating your feet by placing them on another bench, step or chair.

Running Arms

4. Bench curls

For this you will need a bench hooked over some wall bars at about waist height. Hold the other end at a comfortable height using an underhand grip with your elbows straight and your arms in front of your thighs. Then lift the bench up to shoulder height by bending your elbows. Lower the bench back into the starting position and repeat the movement.

If you do not have access to a bench then mimic the action using the water/sand filled drinks bottles mentioned previously.

3. Running arms

Hold a light weight in each hand. These could be plastic drinks bottles filled with water or sand if you have no alternative. Then move your arms forward and back in a rapid running motion. The weights will give extra resistance to the movement and so help to strengthen up the important arm muscles that are used when running.

5. Bench raises

For this the bench should be secured at about shoulder height. Hold the other end at shoulder height with your fingers curled over the top. Then rapidly raise and lower the bench by straightening and lowering your arms. The bench should not go below shoulder height.

As indicated above, water or sand filled drinks bottles may be used as an alternative.

Bench curls

Bench raises

Abdominal exercises

Sit Ups (Hands on Thighs)

1. Sit ups

Lie on the mat with your hips and knees flexed (doing sit ups with straight legs can strain the back). Place your hands on your thighs and then lift yourself up so that your hands touch your knees, then lower yourself back down into the starting position. Repeat the exercise.

If you have fairly strong abdominal muscles you should try to keep your shoulders off the floor between each sit up. If however you are new to

the exercise, then you may need to let them touch the mat between each one.

If you want to make the exercise more difficult, you should place your hands by your ears (instead of on your thighs), but don't pull on your neck as you raise yourself up.

2. Twisted sit ups

This is similar to the straightforward sit up described previously. You start by lying on the mat with your knees and hips flexed and your hands positioned by your ears. As you lift yourself up, try to touch your right knee with your left elbow. Lower yourself back down.

Repeat the exercise, but this time

try to touch your left knee with your right elbow and then lower yourself down. This produces a sit up movement but with a slight twist to alternate sides.

Again, as with the ordinary sit up, you can try to keep your shoulders off the mat between each sit up if you have good abdominal muscles.

Sit Ups (Hands behind Ears)

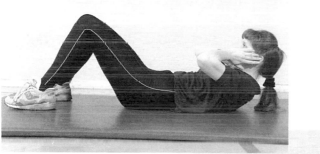

Twisted Sit Ups

Abdominal crunches

3. Abdominal crunches

This is a more difficult exercise and requires good co-ordination.

Start by lying on the mat with your legs almost straight and your hands resting on your thighs. Then raise your upper body as though doing a sit up but at the same time bring your legs towards your body by flexing the knees and hips. Reverse the movement by straightening your legs and lowering your upper body back down onto the mat and into the starting position.

When you become proficient at the exercise, you can try to do it without fully lowering your upper body or legs back onto the mat between each repetition.

4. V-sits

This is similar to the twisted sit up, but it is more difficult. For this exercise you lie on your back with your knees bent and both feet off the ground. Place your hands by your ears and then try to touch your left knee with your right elbow. This is then repeated on the opposite side.

V-sits

Safety considerations

Remember the safety considerations which apply to all exercises of this type, no matter what your fitness or that of the group:

    (i)   Warm up before you start.

    (ii) Start with a number of repetitions you can easily attain without straining and progress gradually.

    (iii) Protect your back.

    (iv) If it hurts, stop.

    (v) Do the exercises regularly.

Chapter 3.5
Stretching for Flexibility and Suppleness
Benefits of being flexible - exercises to include

Benefits of being flexible

Whilst orienteers do not require an extreme range of movement at their joints, the possession of a good level of suppleness and flexibility will certainly help to ensure a fluent running action.

This is because short, tight muscles restrict movement and do not permit the joints to be moved through their full range with ease. Short, tight muscles and tendons are also prone to injury, as they are more likely to be pulled beyond their normal length.

Stretching and general loosening exercises should be undertaken regularly to develop and/or maintain an orienteer's functional level of flexibility. This is best achieved via the inclusion of these exercises as part of your regular warm up routine.

However, if you to develop flexibility as a priority then some additional time should be devoted to it, usually in the form of specific stretching sessions.

Muscles and tendons are most effectively and safely stretched when they are warm, so any stretching should be preceded by a warm up. This may be an active warm up such as a brief jog, or a passive warm up such as a hot bath. Do not follow a passive warm up by any exercise more strenuous than stretching because the high temperatures divert the blood flow towards the skin and away from the muscles. This would cause some conflict in the distribution of the blood if you were to start exercising afterwards and is likely to make the exercise seem far more tiring than usual.

Exercises to include

Exercises to include in a flexibility session are those described for a typical warm up routine in chapter 3.2. However, the duration of the stretch should be held for much longer and each of the exercises repeated two or three times. A routine might include the following:
1. Ankle rotations
2. Hip rotations
3. Spinal rotations
4. Heel raises
5. Calf stretch
6. Calf and Achilles stretch
7. Hip flexor stretch
8. Inner thigh (adductor) stretch
9. Hamstring stretch
10. Quadriceps stretch

Throughout the session, remember the key points about stretching:

1. Warm up thoroughly first. This should be sufficient to induce a slight sweat. If necessary, wear additional clothing. If you start to cool off during the session, do some light aerobic exercise to elevate your temperature once more.

2. All stretched positions should be reached slowly without jerking and then held for at least 10 seconds. When doing these exercises you should feel a comfortable stretch in the muscles. Do not stretch to the point of pain.

3. Do not bounce. Jerking or bouncing movements whilst stretching will cause the muscle fibres to tense up and reduce the effectiveness of the stretch. It can also increase the risk of injury by forcing the muscles beyond their natural length.

Chapter 3.6

The Weekly Training Programme

The weekly cycle - example programmes for M21E - W35 - M45 - W50 - M13 - W11 - recovery from injury programme

The weekly cycle

In the previous chapters of this section we have looked at the various building blocks for an effective training programme - running training, strength training and flexibility work. Now we must consider how these can be fitted together into a coherent whole. It is usual to design training around a weekly cycle.

An effective training programme is not just a random series of training sessions. If you are to get the most out of your training you must consider the content carefully. Think ahead, plan weeks and months in advance as you build up to your goals. Having decided upon (i) the level of fitness you can realistically achieve; (ii) what your strengths and weaknesses are; (iii) the amount of time you can devote to training; (iv) which aspects of fitness you need to work on; and (v) the kind of exercises or training sessions you will need to include, you can now put the programme together.

To help you here are a few examples. But remember when designing your own programme to apply the principles of training and make it specific to your own needs. Finding out about other orienteers' training may give you some ideas, but what they do may not be exactly right for you.

Some example weekly programmes

The following training sessions are based on real examples, although not necessarily those of the individuals pictured.

The content of the programmes should give you some ideas although you may wish to do more or less than what is outlined here.

Remember if substantially increasing your training, build up gradually and don't attempt the full programme in your first week. Start with shorter distances, fewer repetitions and not quite as many sessions:

Example 1 – M21E

Very fit. Specialist sport of orienteering, therefore training is directed towards orienteering specific fitness. Year will be periodised with example below being in the high intensity sport specific phase.

Summary

Distance run 60 - 70 miles. Very fit, training includes a lot of high intensity intervals along with a good volume of training. Plus the use of weights for overall strength.

Sunday
Orienteering race (10 miles)

Monday
Terrain run at steady pace (6 miles)

Tuesday
Interval run 9 x 2 minutes (8 miles)
Circuit training

Wednesday
Steady run (12 miles)
Weight training

Thursday
Hard hill repetitions 8 x approximately 2 minutes (8 miles)
Circuit training

Friday
Run over terrain at moderate pace (12 miles)
Weight training

Saturday
Steady run (8 miles)

Example 2 – W35

Physically very fit, competing most weekends. Training specifically for competitive orienteering.

Summary

Distance run 25 - 30 miles. Much of the training is conducted at a high intensity (intervals and hills) making it very demanding. Plus general conditioning and strengthening work.

Sunday

Orienteering event

Monday

Recovery day - no run
(pm) Multi-gym session for general condition of upper body and abdominals
High repetitions (x30) of each exercise for muscular endurance

Tuesday

(am) Interval run over orienteering terrain (7 miles)
8 minute jog (warm up)
8 x 2 minutes with 1 minute recovery between each. Run on open ground and undulating terrain, avoiding tracks where possible .
Jog to warm down
(pm) Circuit session
12 exercises per circuit
30 secs. per exercise/ 30 secs. recovery
Each circuit completed 3 times

Wednesday

(am) Steady run (6 miles)
Undulating terrain

Thursday

(am) Interval run over hilly terrain (7 miles)
8 minute jog (warm up)
Strides 4 x 100m
8 x 2 minutes with 1 minute recovery between each. Run over tracks, open ground and incorporating as many hills as possible in the efforts.
Jog to warm down
(pm) Circuit session
12 exercises per circuit
30 secs. per exercise/ 30 secs. recovery
Each circuit completed 3 times

Friday

Recovery day - ready for weekend competition

Saturday

Variable; Event if multi-event weekend, or night event (winter), or training orienteering event, or cross-country.

Example 3 – M45
Very fit, training hard for competitive orienteering.

Summary
Distance run 55 - 65 miles. Plus general conditioning exercises. This particular individual finds a relatively high mileage suits him and prefers it to running less distance at a higher intensity. Also completes sets of sit ups, press ups and other general conditioning exercises each day.

Sunday
Orienteering event (8 miles)

Monday
(am) 6 mile run at a steady pace

Tuesday
(am) 8 mile run over orienteering terrain (10 miles)
(pm) 6 mile steady

Wednesday
(am) Steady run (10 miles)
Undulating terrain

Thursday
(am) Interval run over hilly terrain (8 miles)
(pm) 6 miles steady

Friday
(am) Recovery day ready for weekend competition - 5 miles run at easy pace

Saturday
Variable; Event if multi-event weekend or night event (winter) or training orienteering event or cross-country.

Example 4 – W50

Competes in orienteering but has other interests and therefore does not wish to devote all her spare time to training. General wish to maintain a good level of health related fitness as well as running fitness for orienteering.

Summary

Distance run 15 - 20 miles. Plus general conditioning sessions and exercises.

Sunday
Orienteering event

Monday
(am) General daily 'toning' exercises.
(pm) Swim (30 minutes)

Tuesday
(am) General daily 'toning' exercises.
(pm) Steady run (5 miles)

Wednesday
(am) General daily 'toning' exercises.
(pm) Aerobics session

Thursday
(am) General daily 'toning' exercises.
(pm) Steady run (5 miles)

Friday
(am) General daily 'toning' exercises.
(pm) Recovery day ready for weekend competition - no run

Saturday
Variable; Event if multi-event weekend or 3 mile jog

Example 5 – M13

Typically participating in many sports at school and club level. Maintaining a good interest and participation in a broad range of sporting activities. Starting to undertake some specialist running training.

Summary

Distance run 15 - 20 miles, some specialist running training including interval or hill work for strength; plus other sports.

Sunday

Orienteering event

Monday

School P.E.
(After school) basketball club

Tuesday

(Evening) Train with athletic club
5 miles

Wednesday

School - Soccer

Thursday

P.E. - Badminton
(Evening) Train with athletic club, hills or interval session (5 miles)

Friday

Cross country run (3 miles)

Saturday

Variable; Training orienteering event or cross-country.

Example 6 – W11

Mixed interests - the emphasis is on developing a general all round level of fitness, participating in a variety of activities and not specialising at too young an age.

Summary

Weekly distance run about 5 miles, plus mixed sporting activities.

Sunday

Orienteering event

Monday

(Evening) Dance class

Tuesday

School P.E. - netball

Wednesday

Hockey after school

Thursday

Cross country run 2 miles

Friday

Swimming - (1 hour)

Saturday

Gym club, training or squad session.

Example 7 –
Recovery from injury programme

(To be undertaken along with professional treatment prescribed by qualified medical practitioner, physiotherapist, osteopath etc.)

Stage 1

Prescribed period of rest usually a few days but may be longer depending upon the injury.

Stage 2

Adherence to general rehabilitation exercises for strengthening and mobilising the injured area. May also include exercises to prevent the injury from occurring again, if caused by muscular weakness, imbalance or restricted movement. These may need to be undertaken for several days or even weeks before jogging/running commences. They prepare the recovering tissue for the physical stresses of running. If not undertaken, the damaged area will still be weak and vulnerable to further injury.

Stage 3

Reintroduce gentle jogging along with rehabilitation exercises and treatment. This must be gradual to enable the previously injured tissue to adapt to the stresses of running. The return to running should therefore be a gentle jog, not a full competitive event! The duration of the jog must also be realistic. During a five mile run each leg will take about 2500 strides, thus placing stress on the recovering tissue 2500 times; this is not a gradual return to running!

Day 1

Jog very gently for 3 minutes

Day 2

No jog - to see if damaged area has reacted adversely to the exercise, and whether it is ready to take the stresses of jogging.

Day 3

If no adverse reaction jog very gently for 6 minutes

Day 4

If no adverse reaction jog very gently for 10 minutes
An adverse reaction at any stage may require a few days rest and then recommencing the jogging at a level the recovering tissue can withstand.

Day 5

Rest

Day 6

Jog gently for 15 minutes

Day 7

Jog alternate days gradually increasing the time.

Stage 4

Having established that the recovering tissue can withstand gentle jogging without becoming re-injured,

some slightly faster phases of running can be gradually reintroduced into the jogging.

Stage 5

Gradually return to full training with a progressive increase in the duration of each training run, the running speed and the frequency of training.

At each stage the rehabilitation exercises continue as the injury recovers, up to the point where it can withstand the full rigours of training. An adverse reaction to the training indicates that the injured part is not ready to cope with the stresses of running and is likely to be further injured if training is pursued. Thus, resting it for a few days and dropping back to an earlier stage in the jogging programme is advocated.

PART FOUR

Other Factors Affecting Fitness and Performance

Chapter 4.1

Nutrition

Importance of diet - long term nutrition - carbohydrates and fats - proteins - vitamins and minerals - dietary fibre - water - pre-exercise food and drink - dietary manipulation - food and drink during exercise - food and drink after exercise - multi-day events - body composition - nutrition and weight control - healthy fat reduction - summary

The importance of diet

Nutrition is one of the most widely discussed areas of exercise physiology. Questions such as: 'what is a good diet?' and 'which foods should be eaten before training or competitions?' are topics of much debate and controversy. This is perhaps because we all differ slightly in our dietary requirements, we all have our own preferences about what works for us and on occasions we may be misled by general mythology. It is also true that we are subjected to vast amounts of commercial advertising trying to convince us that a particular product is good for us and should be included as

an essential part of our diet, especially if we wish to succeed in our sport.

However, there are a number of guidelines which can be given, enabling the orienteer to make sensible food choices. Nutrition for the sporting individual can be considered under four broad headings:

1. Long term good nutrition.
2. Pre-exercise food and drink.
3. Food and drink during exercise.
4. Food and drink after exercise.

We will also consider how we may influence our body composition or weight by altering our diet.

Long term nutrition

Long term good nutrition is vital for health as well as for optimum sporting performance. This is because the body requires a full range of nutrients to make all the beneficial adaptations and improvements induced by training.

Poor nutrition will prevent the orienteer from training properly and from getting the most out of the training that they do. In extreme cases, poor nutrition can even lead to ill health.

Fortunately the sort of diet that is required by the sports performer is exactly the same as that which is recommended for good health. It should include adequate amounts of carbohydrate, protein, fat, vitamins, minerals, fibre and water. These are the components which make up the food we eat and each of them plays an important role in the basic functioning of the body. We should ensure that we obtain adequate amounts of them in our diet. It is also important that we do not eat too much of them.

For the orienteer undertaking strenuous exercise, some of these food components assume a particular significance. The role of each of these food components is discussed in the following section along with comments on its specific function in relation to exercise and the problems associated with any excesses or deficiencies.

Different foods contain the major components in varying proportions, with bread, pasta and potatoes being high in carbohydrates, whilst dairy products provide a good source of other nutrients. Eating a good balanced mixture of foods can help to ensure that we obtain all the nutrients we need and in the correct proportions. Diets which include only a very limited variety of foods should normally be avoided.

Carbohydrates and fats

If you regularly participate in physical exercise a key requirement is to maintain the muscles' energy stores. The body stores energy in the form of fat and carbohydrate. Fat is stored in various sites around the body, while carbohydrate is stored in the form of glycogen in the liver as well as in the muscles.

When exercising the body uses both fat and carbohydrate, but their relative importance will depend on the intensity of the exercise. Most people in the western world have ample stores of fat (indeed many would benefit if they had a bit less); however, the body's stores of carbohydrate are far more limited and may on occasions become depleted. This is particularly true for those who participate in prolonged forms of exercise such as orienteering.

Carbohydrate comes in two basic forms: simple and complex. The simple carbohydrates are the sugars such as glucose which are found in confectionery, cakes and biscuits. Complex carbohydrate is found in starchy foods such as cereals, bread, pasta and potatoes.

Both sources are ultimately converted into glucose by our digestive system and used by the body in the same way or stored as glycogen in the muscles and liver. Even so, complex carbohydrates are preferable because the starchy foods, which contain complex carbohydrate also contain other important nutrients such as vitamins, minerals, protein and dietary fibre. These are often missing from most sugary foods.

Although it is important not to run out of carbohydrate, it is also important to remember that carbohydrates are high in energy (calories) and it is necessary to maintain a balance between the amount eaten and the number of calories burnt off through exercise. If excessive amounts of carbohydrate are eaten not all of it can be stored as glycogen and the excess will be converted into fat, increasing the body's fat stores. This is another reason for eating complex carbohydrate in preference to sugary foods, as the bulkiness of the food reduces the chances of putting on fat through eating too much.

In contrast, the simple sugars provide a very compact, concentrated form of carbohydrate which can result in taking in too many calories without feeling satisfied or full.

That is not to say you should never eat sugary foods – there are occasions when their rapidly available energy is extremely useful – but you should be careful not to eat too much of them.

Carbohydrates and fats are both used by the muscles as a source of energy. The advantage of using fat as an energy source is that it contains a large amount of energy (calories) in every gram. To store the same amount of energy in the form of carbohydrate (glycogen) would make us prohibitively heavy. However, fat cannot be utilised very quickly and can only be broken down at a rate sufficient to permit a steady jog. It cannot be used rapidly enough to sustain a fast running pace. On the other hand glycogen can be broken down very rapidly and can sustain the energy requirements of fast running. But because we are unable to store large amounts of glycogen it can quickly run out.

To make the most of both fuels they are usually used together. During low exercise intensities, such as gentle jogging, fat is used as the main fuel with just small amounts of glycogen. However, during exercise of a relatively high intensity, carbohydrates become the major fuel.

During such exercise glycogen stores can become depleted. If muscles become low in glycogen then the only remaining energy source is fat. The runner cannot then sustain a fast pace and is forced to slow down, a phenomenon which is accompanied by a fairly distinctive sensation of fatigue. This is the common experience of those suffering from 'glycogen depletion' in the later stages of a long event. The phenomenon is referred to as 'hitting the wall' or having 'bonked' in some endurance sports. In orienteering, it typically occurs 90 - 120 minutes into an event if you have not taken in any additional carbohydrate during the run.

Depletion can also occur over an extended period as a result of several shorter bouts of training or racing. These may have the cumulative effect of using up the body's glycogen reserves if sufficient carbohydrate is not eaten between the sessions. Failing to replenish glycogen stores on a daily basis means that we may start the next training session or event without a full store. If you start an event in this state, you may find yourself becoming fatigued very early on and you will almost certainly find your ability to concentrate affected, especially during the later stages.

In the long term, if the depletion persists due to a diet which is poor in carbohydrate, the additional problems of lethargy, irritability, an inability to exercise properly and an increased susceptibility to illness may also arise.

Glycogen depletion may be of even greater significance in multi-day events where glycogen stores must be replenished overnight if the cumulative effects of several events are not to take their toll.

Whilst the importance of carbohydrate in our diet is paramount, the role of fat should not be overlooked. Fats in addition to being an important source of energy, fulfil a number of other vital functions within our bodies. For example, fat provides insulation, it forms a protective layer around vital organs and is the basis of vital chemicals such as some hormones. A certain amount of fat is therefore essential in our diet and a lack of dietary fat can cause problems.

Most problems, however, arise from eating too much fat and many of us could do with reducing the amount we include in our diets. If we eat too much fat it is stored around our body and makes us heavier without aiding our ability to run. For most of us a reduction in fat stores will not have an adverse effect upon our energy supply as it is our carbohydrate stores which are vulnerable. So from a practical point of view try and cut down on the amount of fat you eat, for both your sports performance and health.

Proteins

Protein is required for the repair and growth of the body. It provides the building blocks for the production of our own proteins, including those which form our muscles, tissues, organs, some hormones and parts of our immune system. Protein can be gained from both animal and vegetable sources with foods high in protein including eggs, meat, fish, poultry, dairy products, soya beans, nuts and other vegetable pulses.

If you do a lot of exercise your protein requirements may increase slightly but it is not necessary to have an extremely high protein diet. Simply eating more food to satisfy your energy requirements should provide your protein needs as well. In fact, if you do eat large amounts of protein, your body will not be able to utilise or store it all and if you eat too much of it, it may be converted into fat.

Eating enough protein is not normally a problem if you are eating a healthy and varied diet. Vegetarians should ensure that they eat a mixture of vegetables, pulses, cereals, and dairy products (or substitutes) at each meal as the proteins contained within them will complement each other.

Vitamins and minerals

Vitamins are essential chemicals which are required for the general mainte-nance of the body, its growth, repair and general well-being. They are involved in numerous chemical reactions which take place within the body. Particular examples are vitamin C and the B vitamins, which are involved in the production of red blood cells and the energy releasing reactions which take place in vast quantities whilst we are exercising.

Since the body is unable to store large amounts of certain vitamins such as (C and the B complex), a regular intake is required. Adequate amounts should be obtained from a sensible varied diet that contains plenty of fresh fruit and vegetables.

It is a mistake to assume that if a little is good, then a lot must be better. Most authorities state that the taking of vitamin supplements is unnecessary if you are eating a healthy diet and, since the vitamins cannot be stored, excesses will be lost in the urine. If your diet is less than adequate, then taking multi-vitamin supplements may help to prevent any potential deficiencies. But this should not be a long term solution and if you think this applies to you, then correcting the underlying dietary shortcoming should be a priority.

Minerals are also required in the general maintenance of the body. They have key roles to play in the structure of certain tissues and the transport of substances around the body. In particular, calcium is needed for the formation of good strong bones and iron is required for the production of haemoglobin, which occurs in the red blood cells that carry the oxygen around the body. Since one of the major affects of regular aerobic exercise such as orienteering is to increase the number of red blood cells and the amount of haemoglobin in the blood, those regularly involved in such sports may require more iron.

It is possible to meet this increased iron requirement by eating a good diet. However, if the amount of iron in the diet proves inadequate – and strict vegetarians may need to take particular care – the body will be unable to increase its haemoglobin levels. In such cases, supplementation may help.

While slight iron deficiency may have only a marginal, though noticeable, effect on your sporting performance, more pronounced iron deficiency can cause anaemia. This manifests itself as feelings of fatigue and lethargy. Women who experience heavy bleeding during menstruation may be particularly prone to these effects.

Other causes of anaemia are known. Those who run high mileages on hard surfaces may experience haemolysis. This is a destruction of the red blood cells due to the pounding of the feet on the ground, and the likelihood of this is increased if inappropriate footwear is worn.

Dietary Fibre

Dietary fibre, also known as 'roughage', is acknowledged to be an important component of the diet in providing the necessary bulk to keep the digestive tract functioning healthily.

Research has indicated that diets which are low in dietary fibre can increase the risk of gastro-intestinal disorders. Vegetables tend to be high in dietary fibre and provide us with a natural source. The intake of roughage may also be increased by eating foods containing 'bran'; certain breakfast cereals are marketed with this aim.

Water

Water is an essential component of our diet. A regular intake is needed to replace the body fluids we lose on a daily basis. This loss is greatly increased through sweating. Therefore when exercising, and particularly if it is hot, you should endeavour to drink plenty of fluids.

In the context of exercise, two of the key functions fulfilled by water are in providing the sweat which cools us, and providing the fluid part of the blood (plasma) which transports oxygen and other nutrients around our body. If you become slightly dehydrated both of these functions are impaired and both sweating rate and blood volume are reduced. This interferes with the effective control of body temperature and reduces your capacity to deliver oxygen to the muscles, which is a key factor in determining your aerobic capacity and ability to sustain a fast running pace. Thus you should drink plenty of water on a regular basis throughout the day to ensure that you are fully hydrated for your training session or competition.

Drinking water during training and competition also has other implications which will be discussed under the section on eating and drinking during an event.

Pre-exercise food and drink

Before an event or training careful consideration should be given to the pre-exercise meal. It is advisable not to eat within 2 - 3 hours of exercise (longer in the case of a larger meal), because food will remain in the stomach for several hours. For example, protein may take 6 hours to digest. Foods high in carbohydrate tend to be easier to digest and are preferable.

When deciding upon a pre-exercise meal you should consider the following factors:

1. Are you familiar with it? Don't try any new foods before a major event; experiment with them in training or on less important occasions.

2. The meal should be easily digestible and eaten several hours prior to the event (depending upon its size).

3. Adequate amounts of liquid should be drunk prior to the event. Many individuals find a light liquid meal most suitable prior to competition.

Dietary manipulation before events ('Carbo-loading')

Whilst an orienteer's diet should always contain large amounts of complex carbohydrate, prior to a long event some individuals participate in various dietary manipulations aimed at increasing the muscles' glycogen stores (and thereby reducing the risk of glycogen depletion during the event). This practice is commonly referred to as 'carbohydrate loading'.

Since hard training will naturally deplete the muscles' stores of glycogen, the simplest way of ensuring that the glycogen stores are full before an event is to reduce the amount of training you do in the days before the event, whilst maintaining a high carbohydrate diet. This 'taper in training'

is what most individuals would do anyway and, if they normally eat a high carbohydrate diet, then the replenishment of the glycogen stores will occur naturally.

The more controversial way of trying to achieve this is via a 'bleed out and loading diet'. Some individuals find this to be effective, but it does have its drawbacks and it is possible to get the timing of it wrong, which can have a negative effect. With this diet there are two stages: the bleed out phase and the loading phase.

During the bleed out phase the individual attempts to completely deplete their muscles of glycogen. Typically this commences 7 - 8 days before the event. It is achieved by initially completing a long run of about 2 hours duration, which will deplete the muscles' glycogen stores. The individual then assumes a low carbohydrate diet and maintains this for the next 3 - 4 days, whilst continuing to run a relatively high mileage.

This ensures that the muscles' glycogen stores are kept low. Then about 3 - 4 days before the event the runner switches to a high carbohydrate diet, eating many small, complex carbohydrate based meals every day. This floods the body with carbohydrate and the muscles, which have been starved of carbohydrate, overcompensate and store an excess of glycogen. This gives the muscles a larger than normal store and reduces the risk of depletion.

Whilst this has been shown to work in controlled experiments and many endurance runners find it to be effective, there are a number of problems. Firstly, during the bleed out phase the low glycogen level makes training very difficult. This can adversely affect the individual's confidence close to the event. It also appears that, when in the depleted state, the individual is more vulnerable to minor infections and viruses, which is again an undesirable situation just before a major competition.

The next problem concerns the timing of the loading phase, which may differ between individuals. For example, if someone takes longer for their muscles to load up with glycogen then they may not be fully loaded by the day of the event. This means that they could start the event in a semi-depleted state, the opposite of what they were trying to achieve.

Alternatively, if you load up more rapidly than expected, you may maximise your glycogen stores several days before the event. Then by the time you come to start the competition, the stores will have returned to normal. The whole process, with all its discomforts, will in this case have been a waste of time. Getting the timing right is therefore essential.

It would also appear that the muscles can only be made to go through this supercompensation and extra glycogen storage a few times a year, so experimenting with the technique becomes difficult. Finally, because the glycogen is stored away with extra water, some individuals experience a heavy legged sensation in their muscles.

So, whilst the bleed out and loading diet is fairly widely practised, it needs to be undertaken with care and for some individuals simply maintaining their high carbohydrate diet and reducing their training can be just as effective, without the unwanted risks.

Alcohol is not recommended

prior to exercise, since not only will it adversely affect your judgment and co-ordination but it will also dehydrate the body and impair its ability to regulate its temperature; factors which will of course be detrimental to performance.

Food and drink during exercise

Before any event your pre-exercise eating and drinking will be important. These should be aimed at ensuring you are fully hydrated, your muscles are fully loaded with glycogen and that your last meal has been sufficiently digested so as not to cause any discomfort.

During short events you are not likely to run out of glycogen if you got your pre-event eating right. However, during a longer event, those approaching two hours, there may be some merit in taking in additional carbohydrate. This could be of greater significance in multi-day events where you may still be semi-depleted from the previous day.

In events where you experience excessive sweating, particularly in hot conditions, you are at risk of dehydration so drinking during the event is advantageous. The stomach absorbs water at a rate of about 0.8 litres an hour. Therefore liquid taken either before or during exercise should be drunk in small doses, as any extra will remain in the stomach and may cause discomfort.

As a suggestion weak glucose solutions could be drunk whilst exercising (approx. 2.5g / 100ml), since this will help to maintain both the blood glucose and fluid levels of the body. Some individuals are under the impression that taking lots of glucose before they start may help them by providing extra energy and increasing their blood glucose levels. However this may not necessarily be the case. Large doses of glucose can cause dehydration and feelings of nausea as they are too strong. So if taking glucose, make sure that it is in a weak solution.

Food and drink after exercise

Following a bout of exercise, such as an event of hard training session. It is important to replace the fluid which has been lost through sweating, and the energy you have burnt up. However, it may be advisable to allow at least one hour to elapse between the exercise and eating a full meal, since this will allow the digestive system to return to a condition in which it can comfortably take the food. Eating too soon after strenuous exercise can cause stomach cramp.

The most important dietary considerations after an event are to ensure a large intake of complex carbohydrate to replenish the glycogen stores in the muscle and plenty of fluids to replace those lost through sweating. Therefore meals based around pasta, bread and potatoes are usually the most effective.

If you have trouble eating a large meal after a hard run you may find eating a couple of small meals more digestible than one massive one. For example, if competing in the morning, try to eat a small carbohydrate based meal within a couple of hours of the event and then a couple more in the afternoon and evening.

Multi Day Events

Replenishment of your carbohydrate stores and fluid levels is of particular significance in multi-day events where, if you fail to refuel with sufficient carbohydrate after one event, you may start the next one without a full store of glycogen in the muscles. You could also be dehydrated; a condition which will also adversely affect your performance. If you think you have difficulties with this, just imagine the problems that the Tour de France cyclists face every day. Basically if they can't get enough carbohydrate and fluid in on one day, they won't last the next.

Body composition

Rather than being worried about your weight, it is probably more appropri-ate to look at your body composition. To do this it is important to differenti-ate between the two. When you weigh yourself, the scales do not distinguish between what is lean body tissue (mus-cle, bone, organs, etc.) and what is fat. Indeed it is quite possible to be the correct 'weight' according to height/weight charts and yet have a poor body composition. Assessing your body composition allows you to iden-tify your proportions of fat and lean tissue. Body composition can be as-sessed using a number of different methods, the simplest being an hon-est look in the mirror.

Alternatively, skinfold thickness can be used. This can be done using calipers or approximated by just using a pinch test. Using your thumb and forefinger, pinch your skin about four inches to the side of your navel, then measure the thickness of the skinfold between your thumb and forefinger. It should be about half an inch thick. If it is more than an inch then perhaps you should consider trying to lose a little fat.

Nutrition and weight control

Although fat is a good source of energy, our fat stores are not normally reduced to levels that prevent vigorous exercise. Conversely, excess fat stored in our bodies can be detrimental to both our health and orienteering performance. Excess fat levels are associated with various forms of cardiovascular disease such as high blood pressure and coronary heart disease.

An increase in your fat stores will also increase your weight making running more difficult. If you are just half a stone overweight imagine running around with three large tubs of margarine strapped to your O-suit. This certainly makes life difficult! Therefore for both good health and orienteering performance, it is important that you are not over fat.

However don't go to extremes. Remember that a certain amount of fat in the body is essential for good health. It is needed for protection, to help maintain your body temperature, as part of the body's structure, for the production of numerous body chemicals such as the steroid hormones, as well as being an energy store.

Healthy fat reduction

The amount of fat we possess depends largely upon the balance between our calorific intake (in the form of food and drink) and our calorific expenditure (in the form of our basic metabolic needs, the physical demands of our work/lifestyle and how much strenuous physical exercise we do). In simple terms if we eat more calories than we burn off then the excess are stored as fat. Conversely if we burn off more than we consume then we are likely to reduce our fat stores as these are used up.

In order to influence our body composition we can alter either side of the equation. If we wish to reduce our stores of body fat we can eat less and/or exercise more. The reverse is also true since if we eat more and/or exercise less then our fat stores will increase.

A healthy sensible reduction in body fat should be achieved by adopting a healthy diet which is high in complex carbohydrate in the form of bread, pasta, potatoes, fruit and vegetables. It should also be low in fat but not completely fat free, for the reasons indicated previously. If coupled with regular training, a loss of 1 - 2lbs a week can be achieved. Anything more than this should be questioned as it can indicate an inadequate intake of certain nutrients and the weight loss may not be in the form of the intended fat but other important factors such as muscle glycogen. Remember glycogen is needed for strenuous exercise and a deficiency will adversely affect training and performance.

People accumulate fat over a prolonged period of time; weeks, months or years. One should therefore be realistic and allow a similar time span in which to lose it. Rapid weight loss conveys a number of risks and is not likely to be conducive to good performance.

105

Remember it is fat reduction which is the key point and not weight reduction. Adopting a healthy diet and exercise regimen can cause no change in weight and in some cases may even produce a slight increase. This is due to the fat lost being accompanied by slight increases in muscle mass,.

This will result in a more toned and slimmer appearance. Shape and body composition may improve even though weight remains static. Such changes are likely to convey very positive health and sporting benefits.

Summary

● Everyone differs in their food and drink requirements.

● Eat what is commonly recognised as a healthy varied diet.

● Ensure that you maintain your glycogen levels through eating complex carbohydrate.

● Keep a careful check on your body composition and how much fat you eat.

● Choose your pre-exercise meal carefully.

● Don't try anything new before an important event.

● Drink plenty of fluids to ensure you are not dehydrated when exercising.

Chapter 4.2:

Injuries and Illness

Types of injury - common orienteering injuries - treatment of orienteering injuries - prevention of injuries - when not to run - running with an injury - running with illness - running when stale - summary

Types of Injury

Virtually all sports convey a slight risk of injury. The only way you can ensure that you don't suffer from a sports injury is not to participate in any sport!

The physical nature of orienteering and the environment in which it takes place almost inevitably results in minor injuries such as scratches, bruises and stings. Few people would class these as sports injuries, unless they were serious enough to prevent them from training or competing. But more substantial sports injuries involving damage to the muscles, tendons, ligaments, joints and bones also occur. These can often cause a lay off from orienteering and since any sports injury is an unwanted inconvenience to the sufferer, it is obviously desirable to minimise their occurrence as much as possible. This section will therefore look at a number of the most common orienteering injuries, their causes and prevention.

Orienteering injuries, like other sports injuries, fall into two broad categories:

1. Traumatic
2. Overuse

Traumatic injuries occur suddenly and can be attributed to a specific incident. They include sprained ankles, pulled muscles, bruises and joint injuries. Commonly they are caused by collisions, falls, rapidly overstretching a muscle or twisting a joint.

Overuse injuries develop over a prolonged period of time. Typically they are first noticed as a slight niggle, an irritation, a slight soreness or a stiffness. In orienteering, joints such as the hip and knee are prone to overuse injuries as are tendons such as the achilles.

Often in the early stages of an overuse injury the symptoms 'go away' as a person warms up or continues with their event. However they will often reappear after the event and get progressively worse as the activity is repeated. Eventually the injury will reach a stage where it starts to inhibit the orienteer from running properly and they realise that they 'have a problem'. This scenario may occur within a single event or quite often it will develop over several weeks.

As the name implies an overuse injury is caused by repetitive actions that result in a body part being overstressed. Often an overuse injury will develop as a result of one or many underlying factors such as running more miles, using worn out running shoes, a change of terrain or the general weakness of a particular body part. Just consider how many times your foot strikes the ground each time you run in an event or go out training.

Any biomechanical imbalance or weakness within the body can be greatly exaggerated by this repetitive action. In addition to this, any slight injury may be aggravated by the repeated stresses placed upon that part of the body. Furthermore, the presence of an injury may cause you to modify your running action to compensate for it and protect that part of the body. This unfamiliar action may then result in abnormal stresses at other joints or muscles causing them to become inflamed and damaged.

Examples of overuse injuries in orienteers include *Achilles tendonitis* (soreness of the Achilles tendon caused by inflammation) and 'shin splints' (a general term used to describe pain in the lower leg which may be due to a number of factors). Additionally, various foot, knee, hip and back 'problems' are also common overuse injuries amongst orienteers.

Common orienteering injuries

Sprained ankle
Damaged knee ligaments and cartilages
Pulled muscles
Achilles tendon strains
Tendon inflammations
Bruises
Compartment syndrome
Broken bones

Ankle injuries

A sprained ankle is a traumatic injury which occurs when the ankle is forced beyond its normal range of movement. This overstretches the ligaments which support and stabilise the joint, causing them to be torn and in some cases severely ruptured. In orienteering, running over uneven ground, brashings and scree all increase the risk of this type of injury. Typically it is the lateral (outer) side of the ankle which is overstretched and hence the ligaments on this side which are torn. However in some cases the medial (inner) side of the ankle can also be damaged if it is compressed when the person 'goes over on their ankle'.

Knee injuries

Another joint which is vulnerable to injury in orienteering is the knee. The normal movement of the knee is backwards and forwards (flexion and extension). These movements are produced by the musculature around the knee, with the direction of movement being restricted by the shape of the bones and other stabilising structures such as the ligaments, cartilages and tendons. These prevent it from bending sideways and twisting to any great extent. However these unwanted movements can occur if the knee is forced in these directions.

Falling is a common cause of knee injuries, especially if the foot remains fixed to the ground as the upper leg rotates or the knee is struck from the side. This kind of scenario can damage the cruciate ligaments of the knee (so called because they form a cross at the back of the knee) and

the ligaments on either side of the knee (lateral and medial). It can also damage the meniscus cartilages of the knee which are positioned between the bones to help stabilise and cushion them.

Blows to a joint such as the knee, caused by falling or hitting a rock can also occasionally result in significant bleeding into the joint. If this occurs it should be treated immediately. If your knee swells up immediately after it's been struck, then it could indicate bleeding into the joint, and a visit to the first aid team would be advisable. Swelling sometime after the incident tends to be caused by other fluids accumulating in the joint and, whilst the injury may still require treatment, it is not likely to be so severe.

Upper leg injuries

A pulled or strained muscle is caused by the muscle's fibres being rapidly stretched beyond their permissible length. This can tear or 'rupture' some of them and as a consequence of this, a certain amount of internal bleeding will occur within the muscle.

In complex movements such as running, the muscles of the legs need to work in a way that enables some of them to relax and lengthen whilst others contract and shorten. This produces the controlled, co-ordinated movement of the leg bones about the ankle, knee and hip joints. For example, in the normal running action the hamstring muscles (at the back of the thigh) have to relax as the knee is brought forward. This relaxation permits them to be lengthened without damage.

When you trip and stumble the leg is brought forward in a very rapid reflex movement to prevent you from falling. The speed of this reflex can mean that the hamstrings are unprepared for the rapid lengthening and may still be tense rather than relaxed. This causes them to resist the movement and can result in some of their muscle fibres being torn as they are forced to lengthen.

A similar situation can sometimes occur when running fast, especially if becoming tired. Here the speed of hamstring relaxation may be too slow, which can again result in torn muscle fibres.

Pulled muscles vary in severity from minor tears, where just a few fibres are damaged, to complete ruptures that will need medical treatment. It is the hamstring (at the back of the thigh) and adductor (inner thigh) muscles which are most commonly damaged by orienteers, although the quadriceps (at the front of the thigh) and calf (lower leg) muscles are also vulnerable.

Colliding with a rock, branch, the ground, or even a fellow orienteer can result in a muscle being bruised. This is because the blow has caused some fibres and blood vessels in the muscle to be compressed and damaged, resulting in bleeding in the region of the damaged tissue. In the case of a bruised muscle this is usually of minor concern. Although it may be stiff for a few days it is likely to heal up relatively quickly and is unlikely to impair your orienteering for any prolonged period.

Lower leg injuries

The most common site of injury in the lower leg is the Achilles tendon. This may be damaged in a traumatic incident where it is rapidly overstretched, causing a partial or full rupture.

Alternatively the injury may be caused by overuse, where the repetitive strain placed upon the tendon causes minute ruptures (focal degeneration), making it sore and vulnerable to further rupture. Another effect of overuse on the Achilles tendon is inflammation (*Achilles tendinitis*). This makes the tendon sore and unable to function properly as it rubs against the surrounding tissues, which can in turn, cause them to become inflamed and complicate the injury (*Achilles peritendinitis*).

It is also possible for other structures such as bursae (fluid filled sacs) around the tendon to become inflamed (*Achilles bursitis*) if they are aggravated by overuse, especially those close to the heel bone.

The calf muscles may be damaged if they are rapidly overstretched, resulting in a pulled muscle. Other calf muscle injuries can cause excessive swelling within the muscles resulting in a cramp like pain (*compartment syndrome*). This is due to the accumulation of fluid in the muscle which is unable to escape (in the case of a torn muscle it will include blood). This causes the muscle to swell until it is restricted by its surrounding sheath.

The continued build up of pressure within the muscle inhibits the flow of fresh oxygenated blood into it. The resulting deprivation of oxygen causes the build up of lactic acid and is felt as a cramping pain. In the case of compartment syndrome this is a more persistent pain which should not be confused with the temporary fatigue that normally accompanies the accumulation of lactic acid during strenuous exercise.

Injuries to the bones

Very occasionally falls and collisions can result in fractures to the bones. In orienteering, fractures to the upper body, limbs and arms appear to be as common as those to the legs. In all cases they will require immediate medical assistance and should be treated using the usual first aid procedures.

The treatment of orienteering injuries

Once you have a sports injury it is advisable to get specialist help as soon as possible. In an ideal situation this would mean within minutes of the injury occurring rather than 48 hours later. Indeed it should be emphasised that immediate treatment can significantly reduce the severity of an injury and the time needed for a full recovery.

As a general rule, don't try to run through an injury as you are likely to make it worse. The application of a cold pack to a pulled muscle, tendon or damaged joint is advocated by most authorities and this should be repeated for the first 24 hours to inhibit bleeding into the damaged tissue. In the case of muscle injuries, elevation and compression are also recommended, as this will further reduce the amount of bleeding into the damaged muscle.

Avoid massage in the initial stages of an injury as this can increase the amount of bleeding. However, once the bleeding has stopped (usually after 24 - 48 hours) massage may then be employed by a therapist to promote the healing process.

Sports injuries are a specialist area, hence the increased number of 'Sports injury clinics' around the country. A good sports injury clinic will employ professionals who spend a lot of time establishing the cause of an injury. It may be surprising to learn that very often the cause and contributing factors to an injury, especially overuse injuries, are not as obvious as it may seem at first.

For example: pain in the hip may be caused by a fault in the running action of the foot; pain in the knee may be aggravated by an imbalance in the strength and flexibility of the muscles around it; and so on. To facilitate an effective recovery and return to orienteering these contributing factors need to be rectified or accounted for, otherwise the injury is quite likely to recur.

Therefore if you visit one of these clinics don't expect an instant diagnosis and be prepared for a lengthy physical examination. As a general rule, if you are serious about getting over an injury, act quickly and seek professional advice as soon as you can.

The prevention of orienteering injuries

With all sports injuries, prevention is better than cure. The more a person trains the more at risk they are from injury (especially overuse injuries).

An orienteer will wish to reduce the risk of both traumatic and overuse injuries as much as possible. Given the nature of the sport it is impossible

to eliminate all risk, even with the best possible preparation and precautions. However, following certain guidelines can help to reduce the risk of an injury occurring and/or its severity.

1. Fitness: Don't attempt to do too much. You will increase the risk of an overuse injury if your body is not used to the amount of exercise you are attempting to do. If you wish to improve your fitness make sure that you increase the amount you do gradually. This is most important after a lay off or when recovering from an injury.

2. Footwear: Ensure that your running shoes are appropriate, giving you adequate support and protection for your running style.

3. Clothing: Wear the appropriate protective clothing. This could include leg cover and gaiters. The use of pro-

tective eye guards are also an idea if you find yourself constantly being hit in the eye by twigs and branches.

4. Current or Previous Injury: Be careful if you have, or are getting over, an injury. Often you will be advised to rest in the initial stages, as exercise may make it worse. Once you are OK to run again don't overdo it.

5. Pain: Don't run with pain. Remember that pain is the body's warning to you that something is wrong. Running with pain can mean that you will make the injury worse. This is always the problem with painkillers, which mask the pain and enable someone to compete when their body would not normally let them do so.

6. Warm up: Warm up gradually before strenuous exercise such as an orienteering event. Both traumatic and overuse injuries are more likely to occur if your body is not physically prepared for the exercise.

Many traumatic injuries are caused by tissue such as muscles, tendons and ligaments being drastically and rapidly overstretched; this causes them to tear. Cold, tight tissues are far more prone to being overstretched and torn than warm tissues, and are thus far more vulnerable to injury. Exercising with cold muscles, tendons and joints is also likely to increase the risk of overuse injuries.

You can therefore reduce the risk of a number of injuries by gently warming up the muscles and joints, for example by jogging to the start, and then stretching them gently before doing any strenuous exercise. This will help to prepare them for the activity by increasing their temperature, helping to increase their natural length and removing unwanted tightness from them.

Gentle stretching will reduce the likelihood of them being damaged by any sudden vigorous stretching that may occur when you run or stumble. A warm up routine will also help to mobilise the joints and can improve the co-ordination of your muscles, thereby making the body less prone to both traumatic and overuse injuries (see the earlier section on warming up for details). A warm up routine should be performed before training as well as competitive events.

7. Other sports: Extra care should be taken when participating in sports that you are less familiar with, since your body may be less well adapted for them and hence you may be even more injury prone than you are when orienteering. Many orienteers get sports injuries when they are not orienteering. Warming up shouldn't be forgotten before the occasional game of squash or football.

When not to run

Most of the time going out training is going to be good for your orienteering, helping you to improve or maintain your fitness. However there are a few occasions when it may be wiser not to train or compete. These occasions can be considered under three headings:

1. Injury
2. Illness
3. Staleness

If you are suffering from any of these then not going out running could be the sensible and more beneficial thing to do in the long term. Always be sensible with your health and fitness. Going out running regardless of your condition could put both in jeopardy.

Running with an injury

The presence of an injury could signal an occasion when training or competition should be missed. If you do consider training or competing with an injury remember that the running could make it worse. In such cases taking a few days off may be preferable to the weeks or even months of inactivity that may result if you aggravate it.

An alternative to taking a complete rest could be to change your activity for a few days. For instance, if you have sore shins then try swimming or cycling. This will take the stress off the injury whilst helping you to maintain your fitness.

For the major traumatic and overuse injuries, it is obvious that you shouldn't run. However, there are many occasions when you have a twinge or slight soreness which you can run with, albeit with some difficulty. These are the occasions when you don't know whether you should run or not.

Unfortunately, there is no set of strict rules or guidelines to help you. Most sports doctors and physiotherapists recommend rest up to a point and then suggest light exercise as part of the rehabilitation process for an injury. The question is when to run and how much?

As a general rule if you have an injury which is causing you discomfort seek the advice of a sports doctor or physiotherapist.

If for some reason this is not practical, try resting it for a few days (injuries take time to heal up so don't expect 24hrs to be sufficient). If it feels all right then try some light training, not a hard session, and build up gradually from there. Listen to your body, pain is a warning mechanism that something is wrong!

One of the problems with an injury is that in the excitement of competition or even in training you don't feel the injury. Warming up will often cause the pain to lessen or go away but not necessarily the injury. Remember that most of us have on occasions finished an event and only then noticed that we have a pain in our leg and have to limp back to the car, or have an impressive set of cuts that we can't remember getting.

Running with an illness

Undertaking strenuous exercise when you have a virus can be a very risky thing to do. This fact was bought closer to our attention by the untimely deaths of some top orienteers in Sweden.

It is a mistake to think that you can 'sweat out an illness' by running hard. What you are more likely to do is to make the condition worse and slow up your recovery. In extreme cases you may even cause yourself long term, and even permanent damage. We all know of people, perhaps even ourselves, who in the past have run when they have been 'under the weather'. With increased medical knowledge, the potential hazards are becoming more clearly understood. The possible consequences of running with a virus, such as the flu are now believed to be quite serious. The most severe problems in this context involve the heart, which can malfunction, be permanently damaged, or even stop functioning altogether with fatal consequences.

A further long term problem which may be caused by exercising with a virus is that of 'post viral fatigue syndrome' and the extreme condition of myalgic encephalomyelitis (ME). The exact details of this condition are still not fully understood, but it would appear that a virus can cause severe fatigue in the victim even when what would normally be unstrenuous physical activity is attempted. This unfortunate condition can last for months or years and is made worse if the victim attempts to return to exercise too soon.

Also associated with viral infections is a general inflammation of body tissues producing a general all over ache and stiffness. This may increase the risk of injury, with the inflamed state of muscles or tendons leading to pulls and strains.

In addition to these risks, if you are suffering from a viral infection such as the flu then you will not be feeling your best, you will feel weak and your concentration may be below par; these are not the ingredients for an enjoyable, successful run. Therefore, for the sake of a few days training or one event, is it worth it?

Following any illness give yourself plenty of time to recover. Don't go out training on the very first day you feel capable. Give yourself a few more days to recuperate and when you do start training again build up gradually. Spend a week or so gradually increasing the distance you cover and the pace you run at. Don't expect to feel fit immediately. You may feel weak for a number of days after the other symptoms of the illness have gone. Running an easier shorter colour course the first time back may be advisable.

So if you have a virus such as the flu then it would be wise to miss a few days training; if you don't then it may force you to miss weeks or even worse. Don't believe that just because you are fit you are invulnerable. Indeed, evidence would suggest that, where as doing a moderate amount of exercise may help to prevent you from becoming ill, overtraining can actually increase your susceptibility to illness.

Running when feeling stale

Staleness is a general term given to the mental and physical state of an individual who may have lost enthusiasm for the sport and/or be performing below expectations for no obvious reason. Staleness is discussed more fully in chapter 4.3.

Summary

● Orienteering is a relatively safe sport when compared to other activities such as team games, racket games, parachuting and horse riding.

● Injuries do occur but by following a few guidelines the risk of these can be minimised and the potential severity of an injury reduced.

● If in doubt about an injury seek expert advice. Don't risk it. The sooner you do something about it the quicker you will recover and get back to full fitness.

● Be careful with your health. Avoid training or competing with a virus. If you are feeling ill, have an injury or just don't feel like going out training then think carefully. A few days off may be just what you need and could prevent a longer, more serious lay off. Of course the difficulty is deciding when the problem is genuine and when you are just being lazy looking for an excuse.

Chapter 4.3

Underperformance, Prolonged Fatigue and Staleness

Underperformance - fatigue - short term acute fatigue - long term chronic fatigue - overtraining and staleness - fatigue as a result of nutritional deficiency - fatigue as a result of illness - sociological pressures - summary

Underperformance

One of the aims of the individual orienteer or coach will be to achieve good, consistent results. If, for no apparent reason, you or your orienteers start to underperform and fail to reach the potential that you or they are capable of, then you must try to find out why and rectify the matter.

Surprisingly the answer is not always more and harder training. Indeed, resolving the causes of a series of poor performances is a complex task, as there may be many underlying factors. The following section attempts to discuss a few of the factors which you should be aware of, how to reduce the risk of chronic fatigue and how to deal with it, should it occur.

Fatigue

Physical stress can have both long and short term consequences upon the body, which can be beneficial or detrimental, depending upon the type and amount of stress.

Firstly it is necessary to differentiate between the type of short term fatigue which is experienced within a single event (acute fatigue) and the more prolonged forms of fatigue which may last several weeks or months, causing a series of poor performances (chronic fatigue).

Short term fatigue (acute fatigue)

Short term fatigue refers to the tiredness experienced during or immediately after a single bout of exercise such as an orienteering event or training session. Sports scientists refer to this as 'acute fatigue'. Acute fatigue is a normal part of any physically demanding sport as it reflects its strenuous nature. In the context of this discussion acute fatigue can be said to be caused by:

(i) A build up of lactic acid

(ii) A temporary depletion of muscle glycogen (an important energy source within the muscles) during a single event

(iii) Dehydration caused by excessive sweating and an inadequate intake of fluid.

Of these, the most immediate cause of fatigue whilst running is the build up of lactic acid. This occurs whilst run-

116

ning fast or uphill or across rough terrain. An aching, burning sensation in the muscles forces the runner to slow down. This form of fatigue is temporary, as the lactic acid is rapidly converted into other compounds within the body as the intensity of exercise eases. It is often experienced many times within a single event or training session.

This form of temporary fatigue is usually beneficial to the body in the long term. The physical stresses it places upon the body act as a stimulus which makes the body adapt to these stresses and improve its overall level of fitness. This is why hard training which causes this form of fatigue brings about improvements in fitness; although it should be emphasised that not every training session has to be made this hard.

The other forms of fatigue which can occur within a single training session or event tend to occur in its later stages. A depletion of the muscles' glycogen stores represents a significant reduction in the amount of energy or fuel available to them. This makes the muscles feel tired and weary as they simply lack the energy needed to work at the same intensity that they were able to at the start of the event or session. This form of fatigue tends to occur in events lasting in excess of 90 minutes and most commonly occurs about 2 hours into an event. In multi-day events it can occur earlier if the muscles have not been able to fully replenish their glycogen stores overnight.

Dehydration is a further potential cause of fatigue. This is where the water lost from the body through sweating reduces the plasma volume

117

of the blood. This has the overall effect of reducing the efficiency of the cardiovascular system. As a result of this the body experiences a sense of fatigue and weariness whilst running, often at slower speeds than it was capable of at the start of the event.

All these forms of short term (acute) fatigue are temporary and the orienteer should recover from them within minutes in the case of lactic acid accumulation, a few hours in the case of dehydration and few hours or perhaps days in the case of glycogen depletion. The exact amount of recovery time needed will of course depend upon the individual, the individual's level of fitness, his or her food and fluid intake and the strenuousness of the event.

If the sensation of fatigue and an inability to compete or train to full capacity persists beyond this, then the underlying cause of fatigue needs to be investigated by the coach.

Long term and persistent fatigue (chronic fatigue)

In all sports everyone has good days and bad days. These fluctuations are to be expected, making sports such as orienteering unpredictable and to a certain extent more competitive.

In some cases a bad day may turn into a string of poor performances. This is not uncommon in sport and you can probably recall phases when you underperformed. Typically you find training is harder than usual and in competition you cannot produce the kind of results that you know you are capable of. The underlying factors behind this may be physical and/or psychological, including:

1. Overtraining, over-competing and staleness
2. Nutritional deficiencies
3. Illness
4. Sociological pressures.

Over-training, over-competing and staleness

The first aspect an individual or coach must consider when confronted with a series of below par performances is the training and racing programme.

Training acts as a stimulus which causes the body to make the physiological adaptations that result in an improvement in fitness. The body needs time to recover from the stresses of training and to make these desired adaptations. If it is not given adequate time in which to do this, its physical condition will start to deteriorate rather than improve. The time needed to recover between hard training sessions (and orienteering events) depends upon their intensity and duration as well as the individual concerned.

The terms 'chronic fatigue' and 'staleness' are used by sports scientists to describe the state of prolonged fatigue which results in a decline in performance and is brought about by overtraining. In addition to affecting the physical condition of the body, overtraining (or over-competing) can also have a significant effect on the psychological state of the performer.

In fact, a need to recover mentally from the stresses of training and competition is as important as the need to recover physically. In support of this there is a considerable volume of evidence to link underperformance with the psychological state of the athlete.

118

Staleness is a very common phenomenon amongst competitors in virtually all sports. One of the physical characteristics of staleness may be a disturbance in some of the hormones of the body, most notably those that are involved in the repair of body tissues and those which are concerned with the breakdown of body tissues. Some of the outward characteristics of staleness include irritability, lethargy, loss of appetite, loss of enthusiasm and spots, as well as the reduction in performance in the sport.

Children can be particularly vulnerable to staleness where, through their own enthusiasms and those of parents or coaches they are overexposed to a sport. As a result they overtrain and over-compete. Their results get worse, so they train harder in order to rectify the problem - causing a vicious circle. In the end they become fed up and disillusioned with the sport.

This is common among top level juniors and may be identified as 'psychological burnout'. However, adults are also afflicted. Any orienteer who has been training and competing hard may benefit from a break, as this will give a period for recovery both physical and mental. If your performance has declined and you suspect over-training or over-competing then a reduction or complete break from training is probably the best course of action. This should be followed by a gradual increase in the intensity and volume of training back up to a level with which you can cope.

Unfortunately, to persuade an orienteer to take a few weeks off is often harder than it seems, even though a short break in these circumstances will almost always result in an improvement in performance.

To minimise the risk of overtraining, you should ensure appropriate rest is incorporated into your training programme. Include specific rest days within a week, easy weeks within each part of the season and a recovery phase within each year. These recovery days and weeks may be in the form of a complete rest from all sport or, in some cases, a change of activity that will help the body to recover. Swimming is often advocated as a good form of 'active rest'.

Planned recovery days and weeks will allow your mind and body time to recuperate, and are an important part of any training programme. So if you start to underperform you should ask yourself these questions:

– When was the last time you had a proper break from training?

– Have you increased your training volume, intensity or frequency over the past few weeks? Remember that it takes time for the body to adapt to training. It may be that you are exceeding your current capacity for training and will need to ease back. Don't forget that orienteering events can be far more strenuous than training and you are likely to require more time to recover from them. All individuals are different and therefore a training programme which works for one person may not be right for another who may have to increase their training load more gradually.

– Are you taking adequate rest before an event such as an easy day or rest day? If not then you could be starting an event semi-fatigued.

– Does your training programme incorporate alternate hard and easy

Fatigue as a result of nutritional deficiency

As stated earlier, depletion of the muscles' glycogen stores within a single event can result in fatigue. In marathon running this is commonly referred to as 'hitting the wall', in fell running it's called 'the bonk' and in various other sports 'the knock'. Under normal circumstance the individual will replenish these glycogen stores quite rapidly through eating a diet which contains plenty of complex carbohydrate (bread, pasta, potatoes etc.) in the days following the event.

In training this is often forgotten and a more gradual form of glycogen depletion can occur with the same fatiguing consequences. For example, if you train hard throughout the week you are likely to be constantly depleting your glycogen stores. A failure to replenish these stores will result in a gradual depletion leading to a lack of energy and the likelihood of complete depletion very early in an event or training session. You may find yourself attempting to train and compete in a semi-depleted state which will cause a degree of tiredness in the muscles and will certainly affect your performance.

If you are underperforming, consider your diet to ensure that you are eating the right kinds of food. Any orienteer who is on a calorie restricted diet, for example when attempting to lose weight, will be prone to a shortage of carbohydrate and therefore vulnerable to this form of fatigue. Even those who are not attempting to lose weight may still be short of carbohydrate, especially if eating the wrong types of food. Therefore an emphasis

days so as to facilitate recovery from the hard training? The easy day may be in the form of a steady run or a complete rest.

All orienteers must respond to the signals their body gives them. If you are feeling tired and listless, then a hard session may not be the best thing for you to do. In this context it is necessary to differentiate between genuine prolonged fatigue and a small amount of apathy when confronted with the prospect of a hard training session.

In addition to its direct effects in fatiguing the mind and body, overtraining can also lead to a number of other states which cause fatigue and underperformance. These include: nutritional depletion, overuse injuries and illness.

on the inclusion of high carbohydrate foods, such as bread, pasta and potatoes in the diet is important. Once again a rest day in a training programme could be advocated as it will provide the opportunity for the muscles to replenish their glycogen stores.

One of the adaptations the body makes to training is to increase the number of red blood cells which transport oxygen around the body. Unfortunately, there is some evidence to suggest that running a high mileage on hard surfaces can actually damage the red blood cells, due to the pounding they receive when passing through the soles of the feet. This destruction of red blood cells will obviously be in conflict with the body's desire to increase their number. If a runner's diet is deficient in iron (iron is essential in the manufacture of red blood cells) the body will be unable to manufacture the red blood cells it needs.

This will limit the body's ability to deliver the required oxygen to the muscles, thus increasing the likelihood of fatigue. Iron deficiencies can occur in both males and females but tend to be more common in female runners who lose iron through the blood loss associated with menstruation.

A deficiency in iron is referred to as anaemia and in runners it may be difficult to diagnose for a number of reasons. Firstly, the degree of anaemia may be slight; to the extent that it would not be noticed if the individual were not involved in a strenuous sport. Secondly, one of the effects of training is to increase the plasma (fluid part) volume of the blood. This has the overall effect of diluting the blood, despite the fact that training increases the number of red blood cells. This

dilution can result in a form of pseudoanaemia, which is not a true anaemia but can confuse the diagnosis.

An orienteer who is fatigued, lacks energy and is underperforming, could consider taking iron supplements, either separately or as part of a multi-vitamin complex. In either case the iron should be taken with orange juice, as the vitamin C contained within the juice will help with the assimilation of the iron into the body. In addition to this a blood test may be advocated as a precautionary measure for detecting anaemia and/or other blood disorders.

An overall healthy diet is essential for anyone participating in sports such as orienteering. A good diet enables an individual to train and com-

121

pete. If your diet is poor then you will not have the energy or physiological capacity to train hard and compete to their potential. With a few possible exceptions dietary supplements should not be relied upon to make up for a poor diet.

Fatigue as a result of illness

Specialists in sports medicine are becoming increasingly aware that certain illnesses can have a prolonged fatiguing affect upon the body. These include glandular fever and a number of diseases which can cause 'post viral fatigue syndromes', which for the orienteer can mean a general feeling of fatigue whilst training or competing. Perhaps the most commonly discussed of these is Myalgic Encephalomyelitis (ME).

Whilst these disorders may be the underlying cause of prolonged fatigue in some cases, the coach has to be careful not to attribute all cases of underperformance to them. In situations where an illness or post viral fatigue syndrome is suspected expert medical advice is advocated.

An orienteer should not attempt to train through an illness. It is likely to make your condition worse rather than better. In general terms a short lay off is the usual and most effective prescription.

It is also interesting to note at this point that overtraining with its associated excessive physical and mental stress is believed to cause the suppression of the body's immune system. This makes a person more vulnerable to illnesses such as viruses. Coaches must therefore watch out for individuals who frequently suffer from illnesses, as this may be an indication of overtraining.

Sociological pressures

Sometimes when looking for the underlying causes of fatigue and a reduction in performance you have to look outside your sport and training.

All orienteers are subject to other pressures, including exams, family issues, financial, social and personal matters. Each of these can affect your psychological state and hence your performance, due to the additional stresses you must deal with. So think about the other factors in your life which could be affecting your orienteering and general well-being.

Summary

● There are many potential causes of prolonged fatigue and underperformance. Factors which should be considered are:
   (i) the training programme
   (ii) nutrition
   (iii) illness
   (iv) factors external to orienteering
   (v) rest.
● The key to an improved performance is not always more training; indeed often the reverse is true.
● Rest days can help to prevent staleness, injury, glycogen depletion and illness.
● It is important to be aware of your own training capacities, and not to exceed them.
● Plan your training to get fit for orienteering. So train hard but remember to give your body the rest it needs to recover and respond to the training stimulus you give it.

PART FIVE

Time for Action

Chapter 5.1
Time for Action

Knowing how to improve your fitness will not benefit your orienteering unless you act upon that knowledge. So now is the time to put it into practice.

There is no absolute right or wrong way to train. You must consider what works best for you. I hope that reading this book has at least caused you to think about your training. Hopefully you will feel inspired to train harder and better, although you may of course feel reassured that your training is already appropriate for your needs.

Remember when planning your fitness programme to start gradually and not to let your enthusiasm cause you to attempt to increase your training by too much too soon. Listen to what your body is telling you; train hard when you are able, but ease back if you need a rest. Work towards your goals but don't take risks with your health. We all hope to have many years of competitive orienteering ahead of us and it's not worth gambling it all for the sake of one event or one training session.

Good luck with the training and if some of the advice given here assists you in beating me, I will not be *too* disappointed!

Further Reading

Bagness, M. Outward Bound Orienteering Handbook (1995), London, UK: Ward Lock

Hazeldine, R. Fitness for Sport (1985), Marlborough, UK: Crowood Press

McNeill, C. Orienteering The Skills of the Game (1989), Marlborough, UK: Crowood Press

Milroy, P. Sports Injuries (1995), London, UK: Ward Lock

Newsholme, E. Leech, T and Duester, G. Keep on Running. The science of training and performance (1994). Chichester, UK: Wiley and Sons

Smith, B. Flexibility for Sport (1995), Marlborough, UK: Crowood Press

Wooton, S. Nutrition for Sport (1989), London, UK : Sportspages

Acknowledgements

Thanks to Hazelle Jackson and Ned Paul of *CompassSport* magazine for their expertise, help and advice throughout the production of this book. Some of the material has previously appeared in a different format in *CompassSport* magazine.

Thanks for the photographs to Rod Organ (cover), Hazelle Jackson (pp 6, 8, 10, 12, 13, 14, 15, 21, 22, 23, 26, 31, 39, 40, 44, 48, 58, 59, 60, 83, 85, 87, 88, 91, 92, 94, 95, 97, 101, 104, 106, 109, 112, 117, 120, 121, 124), Mark Roberts (pp 49, 50, 52, 53, 54, 55, 56, 57, 58, 70, 71, 72, 73, 74, 75, 76, 77, 78, 79, 80, 81), Steve Bird (p86), and Jackie Bird (back cover).

Thanks to all those appear in the photos unwittingly or not especially Alison Mackenzie, Louise Mansfield, Meirion George and Hugh Marsden.

Special thanks to Jackie Bird and also all the colleagues who have supported me in this venture.

Useful Addresses

British Orienteering Federation, 'Riversdale', Dale Road North, Darley Dale, Matlock, Derbyshire, DE4 2HX

National Coaching Foundation, 114 Cardigan Road, Headingley, Leeds, LS6 3BJ

National Sports Medicine Institute, Charterhouse Square, London, EC1M 6BQ

British Association of Sport and Exercise Sciences, 114 Cardigan Road, Headingley, Leeds. LS6 3BJ

International Orienteering Federation, PO Box 76, 191 21 Sollentuna, Sweden

Orienteering Association of Australia, P.O. Box 263, Jamison Centre, ACT 2614, Australia

Canadian Orienteering Federation, 1600 James Naismith Drive, Gloucester, Ontario, K1B 5N4

Irish Orienteering Association, House of Sport, Longmile Road, Walkinstown, Dublin 12, Ireland

New Zealand Orienteering Federation, P.O. Box 19312, Hamilton, New Zealand

United States Orienteering Federation, PO Box 1444, Forest Park, GA 30051, USA

Dedication

To sunlit forests, the smell of pine, open moorland, good competition and
great camaraderie and that elusive error free run!